IIS
11108

D1632810

for **AQA**

WITHDRAWN

AS BIOLOGY

Revision Guide

David Applin

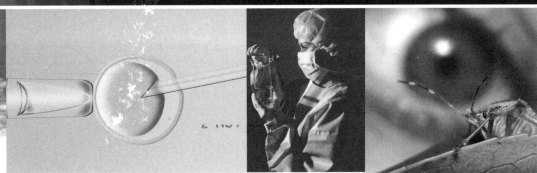

WITHDRAWN

OXFORD
UNIVERSITY PRESS

OXFORD

Great Clarendon Street, Oxford OX2 6DP

Oxford University Press is a department of the University of Oxford.
It furthers the University's objective of excellence in research, scholarship,
and education by publishing worldwide in

Oxford   New York

Auckland   Cape Town   Dar es Salaam   Hong Kong   Karachi
Kuala Lumpur   Madrid   Melbourne   Mexico City   Nairobi
New Delhi   Shanghai   Taipei   Toronto

With offices in

Argentina   Austria   Brazil   Chile   Czech Republic   France   Greece
Guatemala   Hungary   Italy   Japan   Poland   Portugal   Singapore
South Korea   Switzerland   Thailand   Turkey   Ukraine   Vietnam

© Oxford University Press 2008

The moral rights of the author have been asserted

Database right Oxford University Press (maker)

First published 2008

All rights reserved. No part of this publication may be reproduced,
stored in a retrieval system, or transmitted, in any form or by any means,
without the prior permission in writing of Oxford University Press,
or as expressly permitted by law, or under terms agreed with the appropriate
reprographics rights organization. Enquiries concerning reproduction
outside the scope of the above should be sent to the Rights Department,
Oxford University Press, at the address above

You must not circulate this book in any other binding or cover
and you must impose this same condition on any acquirer

British Library Cataloguing in Publication Data

Data available

ISBN 978-0-19-915268-1

10 9 8 7 6 5 4 3 2 1

Printed in Great Britain by Bell and Bain Ltd, Glasgow

Paper used in the production of this book is a natural, recyclable product made from
wood grown in sustainable forests. The manufacturing process conforms to the
environmental regulations of the country of origin.

Acknowledgements

Although authors write in isolation, each book is the result of team effort. It is therefore a
pleasure to acknowledge the colleagues who have contributed to this work, especially: Eileen
Ramsden, author and formerly of Wolfreton School, Hull; Peter Marshall, former Head of
Biology the Leys School, Cambridge; Piers Wood, tutor Mander Portman Woodward, Cambridge;
Douglas Griffiths, tutor St Andrew's Tutorial College, Cambridge; John Mullins of St Ivo School,
Cambridgeshire. To them all, grateful thanks for many discussions and ideas. Particular thanks
are due to my editor Sarah Ware whose patience and sympathetic handling of the manuscript
have ensured that this Revision Guide is student-friendly throughout and a highly effective
resource for learning and revision. Finally the unstinting support of my family helped to ensure
a successful conclusion to the project.

D G Applin

Cambridge, July 2008

Diagrams p60 (2.05 meiosis), p62 (2.06 the founder effect), p72 (2.11 mitosis), and p86
(2.17 water transport diagrams) © David Applin.

LIBRARY
NEWCASTLE COLLEGE
NEWCASTLE UPON TYNE

Class 57 4

BARCODE 0216 7697

Contents

Introduction

I hope that *AS Biology for AQA Revision Guide* helps you to do well in your examinations. Although these are an important goal they are not the only reason for studying Biology. I hope also that you will develop a real and lasting interest in the living world which studying Biology will help you to understand. If you enjoy using this book then all the effort of writing it will have been worthwhile.

Getting the most out of this Revision Guide

This *Revision Guide* covers the subject content of the specification for the AQA AS Biology award 1411 examinable from 2009. It is not intended to replace textbooks and other learning resources but rather to provide succinct coverage of all aspects of the AQA specification, AS Biology.

It is written to be accessible to all students. You will find it useful whether you wish to continue studying Biology after AS or want to achieve as high a grade as possible at AS, as part of a suite of qualifications suitable for continuing studies in other areas.

The *AS Biology for AQA Revision Guide* departs from textbook style. Where appropriate, content is presented as annotated diagrams, flow charts and graphics integrated with easy-to-read text which nevertheless maintains standards of accuracy and scientific literacy which will enable you to obtain the highest grade possible in your exams. It includes the latest developments in the biological sciences.

- **Special features** – The different features of the *Revision Guide* are explained on the facing page. These will help you to get the most out of the book.

- **Revising successfully** – Page 6 gives you helpful tips on how to organize your revision, make the most of your time, and different strategies to help you recall what you have learned.

- **Assessment for AS Biology** – Pages 6 and 7 set out the structure of the AS Biology qualification for AQA, and marks allocated to each part of the assessment process. It will help you understand the different areas covered in the Specification and the skills you require. It also gives some helpful tips for answering questions and maximizing your marks.

- **Making links** –A series of spider diagrams on pages 8 and 9 guide you through units 1 and 2. They bring together the main biological themes of the AQA specification with reference to relevant pages in the *Revision Book*. You can use these to record your revision as you go along, by colouring the 'arms' to highlight your progress.

- **End of unit questions and answers** – Test yourself at the end of each unit with further questions at the back of the book (pages 98–101). A guide to the required answers is given on page 102.

Good luck with your exams!

David Applin

Special features

As you use the *Revision Guide* you will notice different features. These will help you to focus on important points and guide your revision.

- **Objectives** at the beginning of each section list the specification content covered in the section.

- 'Before you start...' points you to other parts of the *Revision Guide* where related topics are explained.

- **Key words** are highlighted in **bold** in the text. You will find all words in the index are **bold** in the text, helping you to identify them at a glance.

- **As a result** provides an explanation which arises from a sequence of linked facts or processes.

- 'Notice' in the text draws your attention to important facts which are illustrated in a diagram, graph, or table.

- 'Remember' prompts you to recall facts relevant to the content you're revising.

- **Fact file** provides interesting points related to specification content for you to note.

- **How science works** is an important feature of the new specifications. The concept follows on from your work at GCSE. It focuses on the processes of scientific enquiry and the implications of scientific developments for society. The *Revision Guide* provides a selection of examples which follow the criteria A–L listed in 3.7 of the specification.

- **Qs and As** offer the opportunity to ask a question and provide a model answer relevant to an aspect of the specification that might cause confusion when answering exam questions.

- **Questions** at the end of each section test your knowledge and understanding of the content of the section you're revising.

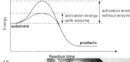
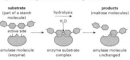

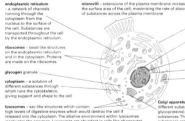

Revising successfully

To be successful in AS level Biology you must be able to:

- recall information
- apply your knowledge to new and unfamiliar situations
- carry out precise and accurate experimental work
- interpret and analyse your own experimental data and that of others

Careful revision will enable you to perform at your best in your examinations. Work with determination and tackle the course in small chunks. Make sure that you are active in your revision – just reading information is not enough.

Useful strategies for revision

As well as reading this *Revision Guide*, you might like to use some or all of the following strategies:

- Make your own condensed summary notes.
- Write key definitions onto flash cards.
- Work through facts until you can recall them.
- Ask your friends and family to test your recall.
- Make posters which cover items of the specification for your bedroom walls.
- Carry out exam practice.

Measure your revision in terms of the progress you are making rather than the length of time you have spent working. You will feel much more positive if you are able to say specific things you have achieved at the end of a day's revision rather than thinking 'I spent eight hours inside on a sunny day!' Don't sit for extended periods of time. Plan your day so that you have regular breaks, fresh air, and things to look forward to.

How to use the spider diagrams

Pages 8 and 9 provide you with spider diagrams that make links between main biological themes of the AQA specification and relevant pages in this *Revision Guide*.

- Start by reading the diagrams and highlighting those areas which you are confident about already. For these sections you can move straight to the relevant

pages, quickly read through the material, and test your understanding by working through the questions.

- Then start working on the sections that you haven't highlighted. Work carefully through the material on each page, colour key definitions and highlight important diagrams. Constantly test your recall by covering up sections and writing them from memory.
- Once you have worked through a section, highlight it on the diagram. The more colour on your diagram, the more work you have done to prepare for your examination. By doing this you will feel positive about what you have achieved rather than negative about what remains to be done.

How to improve your recall

Here's a good strategy for recalling information:

- Focus on a small number of facts. Copy out the facts repeatedly in silence for five minutes then turn your piece of paper over and write them from memory.
- If you get any wrong then just write these out for another five minutes.
- Finally test your recall of all the facts.
- Come back to the same facts later in the day and test yourself again.
- Then revisit them the next day and again later in the week.

By carrying out this process the facts will become part of your long-term memory – you will have learnt them!

Once you have built up a solid factual knowledge base you need to test it by completing some past papers for practice. It might be a good idea to tackle several questions on the same topic from a number of papers rather than working through a whole paper at once. This will enable you to identify your weak areas so that you can work on them in more detail.

Finally, remember to complete some mock exam papers under exam conditions.

Assessment for AS Biology

The table below shows how the marks are allocated in the AQA AS Biology course. Notice that unit 1 has a lower mark allocation than unit 2. This is so that unit 1 may be taught in the autumn term of year 12. Students may then sit the unit 1 examination in January. Alternatively students may sit both units 1 and 2 in June.

Unit	Name of unit	Method of assessment	% of AS exam
1	Biology and disease	Exam 1 hour 15 minutes 60 raw marks (100 UMS)	33.3
2	The variety of living organisms	Exam 1 hour 45 minutes 85 raw marks (140 UMS)	46.7
3	Investigative and practical skills in AS Biology	Assessed during the course. If your work is internally marked (the Centre Marked Route) you will complete two components: • Practical skills assessment (PSA) • Investigative skills assignment (ISA) If your work is externally marked (the Externally Marked Route) you will also complete two components: • Practical skills verification (PSV) • Externally marked practical assignment (EMPA) For either route there are 50 raw marks (60 UMS).	20

Assessment Objectives

Each of these units will examine your ability to meet the assessment objectives below. Work through the statements and highlight the key words. Note that these are skills not lists of content.

Assessment objectives one and two are assessed across all units while assessment objective three is assessed mainly in unit three.

Assessment Objective One – Knowledge and understanding of science and of *How Science Works*

You should be able to:
- recognize, recall, and show understanding of scientific knowledge
- select, organize, and communicate relevant information in a variety of forms

Assessment Objective Two – Application of knowledge and understanding of science and of *How Science Works*

You should be able to:
- analyse and evaluate scientific knowledge and processes
- apply scientific knowledge and processes to unfamiliar situations, including those related to issues
- assess the validity, reliability, and credibility of scientific information

Assessment Objective Three – *How Science Works*

You should be able to:
- demonstrate and describe ethical, safe, and skilful practical techniques and processes, selecting appropriate qualitative and quantitative methods
- make, record, and communicate reliable and valid observations and measurements with appropriate precision and accuracy
- analyse, interpret, explain, and evaluate the methodology, results and impact of your own and others' experimental and investigative activities in a variety of ways

Quality of Written Communication (QWC)

You should:
- ensure that text is legible and that spelling, punctuation, and grammar are accurate so that meaning is clear
- select and use a form and style of writing appropriate to purpose and to complex subject matter
- organize information clearly and coherently, using specialist vocabulary where appropriate

Quality of written communication is assessed across all units; if you write clear, well explained answers then you should obtain any marks assigned to it.

Investigative and practical skills

Your school will decide if your work is to be internally or externally marked – this has no impact on the work you will complete but does make the system appear slightly more complicated.

Answering exam papers

When you look at your exam paper read through all the questions. Identify which are the easiest for you to answer. Start by answering these questions.

Remember to read each question carefully and make sure you are answering the question that is actually set and not the one you would like to be set. Remember to look at the number of marks available for each question and tailor the number of points you make in your answer accordingly. *Do not* write an essay for a question that only attracts one or two marks!

With short-answer questions, look at the amount of space that has been left for the answer. This indicates the length of answer that the examiner anticipates you to give – depending on the size of your handwriting, of course.

Make every effort to answer all the questions. An unanswered question will always score 0! If you can, leave enough time to check through your answers at the end.

Here are some popular words which are often used in exam questions. Make sure you know what the examiner means when each of these words is used.

- **Describe** – Write down all the key points using words and, where appropriate, diagrams. Think about the number of marks that are available when you write your answer.

- **Calculate** – Write down the numerical answer to the question. Remember to include your working and the units.

- **State** – Write down the answer. Remember a short answer rather than a long explanation is required.

- **Suggest** – Use your biological knowledge to answer the question. This term is used when there is more than one possible answer or when the question involves an unfamiliar context.

- **Sketch** – When this word is used a simple freehand answer is acceptable. Remember to make sure that you include any important labels.

- **Define** – Write down what a biological term or statement means.

- **Explain** – Write down a supporting argument using your biological knowledge. Think about the number of marks that are available when you write your answer.

- **List** – Write down a number of points. Think about the number of points required.

- **Discuss** – Write down details of the points in the given topic.

Biology and disease

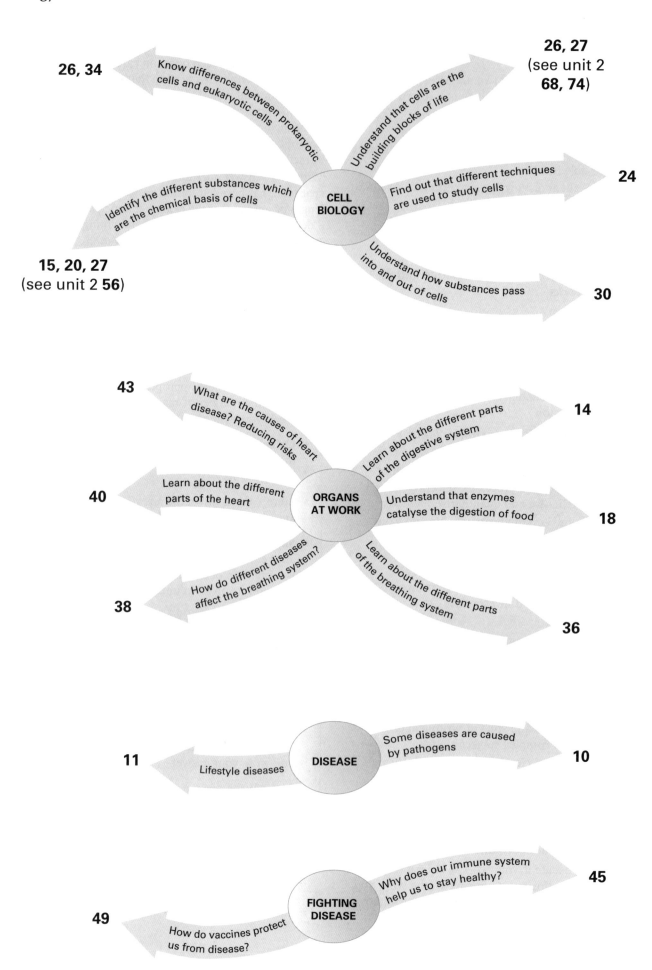

26, 34 — Know differences between prokaryotic cells and eukaryotic cells

Understand that cells are the building blocks of life — **26, 27** (see unit 2 **68, 74**)

Find out that different techniques are used to study cells — **24**

CELL BIOLOGY

Identify the different substances which are the chemical basis of cells — **15, 20, 27** (see unit 2 **56**)

Understand how substances pass into and out of cells — **30**

---

43 — What are the causes of heart disease? Reducing risks

Learn about the different parts of the digestive system — **14**

Learn about the different parts of the heart — **40**

ORGANS AT WORK

Understand that enzymes catalyse the digestion of food — **18**

How do different diseases affect the breathing system? — **38**

Learn about the different parts of the breathing system — **36**

DISEASE

Lifestyle diseases — **11**

Some diseases are caused by pathogens — **10**

FIGHTING DISEASE

Why does our immune system help us to stay healthy? — **45**

How do vaccines protect us from disease? — **49**

Making links: unit 2

The variety of living organisms

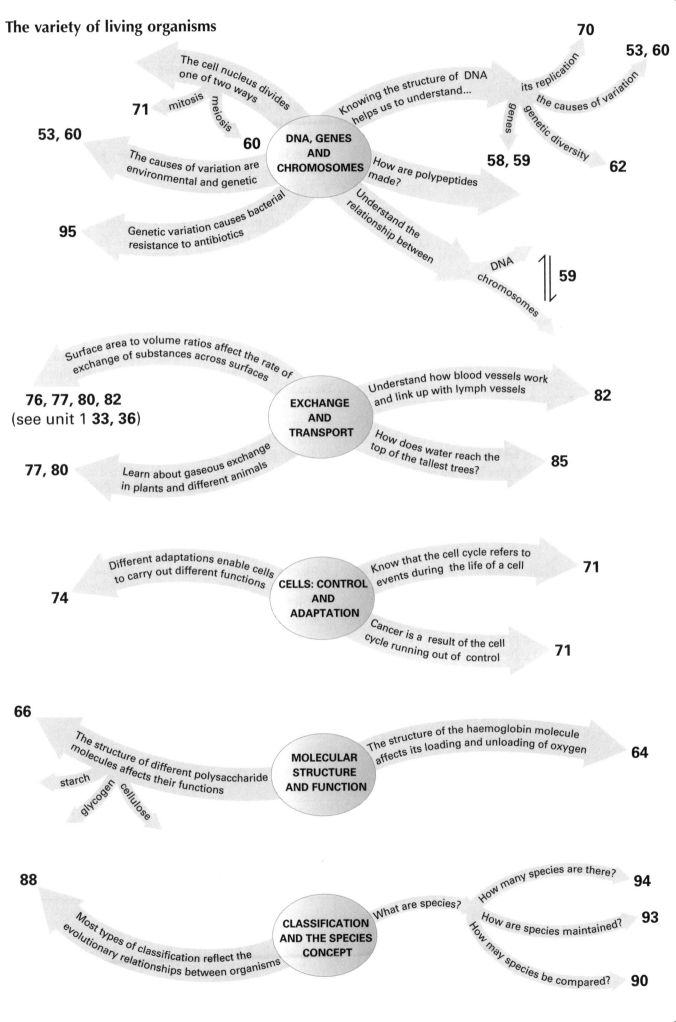

70

53, 60

The cell nucleus divides one of two ways

Knowing the structure of DNA helps us to understand...

71 mitosis meiosis

its replication

the causes of variation

53, 60

60

genes

genetic diversity

The causes of variation are environmental and genetic

DNA, GENES AND CHROMOSOMES

How are polypeptides made?

58, 59

62

95

Genetic variation causes bacterial resistance to antibiotics

Understand the relationship between

DNA chromosomes

59

Surface area to volume ratios affect the rate of exchange of substances across surfaces

Understand how blood vessels work and link up with lymph vessels

82

76, 77, 80, 82
(see unit 1 **33, 36**)

EXCHANGE AND TRANSPORT

77, 80

Learn about gaseous exchange in plants and different animals

How does water reach the top of the tallest trees?

85

Different adaptations enable cells to carry out different functions

Know that the cell cycle refers to events during the life of a cell

71

74

CELLS: CONTROL AND ADAPTATION

Cancer is a result of the cell cycle running out of control

71

66

The structure of different polysaccharide molecules affects their functions

The structure of the haemoglobin molecule affects its loading and unloading of oxygen

64

starch glycogen cellulose

MOLECULAR STRUCTURE AND FUNCTION

88

How many species are there?

94

Most types of classification reflect the evolutionary relationships between organisms

What are species?

CLASSIFICATION AND THE SPECIES CONCEPT

How are species maintained?

93

How may species be compared?

90

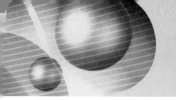

1.01 Pathogens and disease

OBJECTIVES

By the end of the section you should

○ *know that some bacteria, viruses, and fungi are pathogens*

○ *understand that to cause disease pathogens must attach to or penetrate body surfaces*

○ *know that pathogens cause disease by damaging the host's cells and by producing toxins*

Before you start, it will help to read sections **1.13** (cholera) and **1.18** (T cells).

Organisms that cause disease are called **pathogens**. They include different types of **bacteria**, **viruses**, and **fungi**. When the human body is their host, they may make us ill. The body is warm and moist – an ideal environment for pathogens to grow, multiply, and spread.

Penetrating body surfaces

Pathogens can cause disease when they penetrate any of the body's interfaces with the environment. These include surfaces within the digestive and gas-exchange systems. Invading pathogens must first attach to the cells of body surfaces or penetrate the cells themselves. They must also survive the host's defences against their invasion.

- Substances produced by bacteria enable them to bind with surface receptors on the cell surfaces of the host's tissues.
- Extensions of the plasma membrane enable some types of bacteria to attach to the host's tissues.
- Enzymes produced by bacteria enable the cells to enter the host's tissues. Their activity breaks down the tissues, allowing deep penetration. Other enzymes destroy the white blood cells of the host's immune system.
- A tough outer layer covers many types of bacterial cell. The layer protects the cell from the host's white blood cells. Loss of the layer makes the bacterium vulnerable to the host's defences. It is destroyed before it causes disease.

How do pathogens cause disease?

Pathogens cause disease by producing toxins and by damaging the cells of the host's tissues. For example, bacteria produce two types of toxin – exotoxins and endotoxins.

Exotoxins are mostly proteins and very potent in small amounts. For example:

- The bacterium *Corynebacterium diphtheriae* causes diphtheria. It produces a toxin that prevents protein synthesis in the host's cells. The toxin molecule is in two parts – one part causes the toxicity; the other part promotes uptake of the molecule by host cells. The toxic part causes a swollen throat and massive internal bleeding.

Endotoxins are part of the bacterial cell surface membrane. They are less potent than exotoxins but can be lethal. For example:

- The endotoxin of *Escherichia coli* can cause a sudden decrease in blood pressure leading to septic shock.

Damage to the host's tissue may be direct or indirect. For example:

- **Human immuno deficiency virus (HIV)** directly attacks the T-helper cells of the immune system, destroying them. The body's immune response to infections is weakened. People infected with HIV do not suffer from the effects of the virus itself but from the different pathogens which gain a foothold once HIV has destroyed sufficient numbers of T-helper cells.
- *Mycobacterium tuberculosis* causes tuberculosis. The damage to lung tissue is indirect. The bacterium triggers an immune response by the host. Phagocytic cells gather where the bacterial cells have infected cells of the lungs and release enzymes. The enzymes break down the lung cells, damaging the tissue.

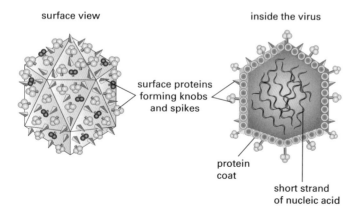

The knobs and spikes on this virus help it to bind with the host cell.

Questions

1 What are pathogens?

2 How do pathogens cause disease?

3 How does lung tissue become damaged when infected with the bacterium which causes tuberculosis?

1.02 Lifestyle diseases

O B J E C T I V E S

By the end of the section you should

○ *know that lifestyle can affect human health*

○ *understand the idea of risk factors*

○ *be able to identify lifestyle changes which reduce risk*

○ *be able to recognize correlations and causes*

Before you start, it will help to read sections **1.17** (heart disease), and **2.01** (mutations).

Lifestyle diseases and risk factors

The UK has a highly developed economy. More money means that more people are able to spend more on **lifestyle** (the way a person lives their life). People who pursue an unhealthy lifestyle are at greater risk of developing particular diseases than people who choose more healthy options.

Cancer and disease of the heart and blood vessels are examples of so-called **lifestyle diseases**. Today they account for the majority of deaths in the UK.

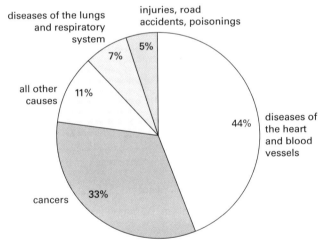

Causes of death in people aged under 75 in the UK

Life is uncertain. What we do might increase the chances of something happening to us. 'What we do' is our lifestyle. Choice of lifestyle can affect our health.

• If what we choose to do increases the chances of ill health, then the choice is a **risk factor**.

• Not making the choice removes the risk, so some risk factors are **avoidable**.

• **Unavoidable** risk factors are associated with events over which we have no choice. Ageing, gender, and the genes we inherit are important examples. They set the risk rate of our developing particular illnesses.

You do not need to learn the charts and graphs in this section, but you may need to interpret them (or similar) in an exam.

Smoking and heart disease

In the UK 114 000 people die early each year because of the chemicals they inhale in cigarette smoke – in particular **nicotine** and **carbon monoxide**. Heart disease accounts for 27% of these early deaths.

• Nicotine raises **pulse rate** and **blood pressure**, increasing the risk to smokers of developing heart disease.

• Carbon monoxide combines with **haemoglobin** in red blood cells, reducing the capacity of the cells to absorb oxygen. The heart has to work harder to supply blood (and the oxygen it carries) to the tissues of the body.

The combined effects mean that smokers of all ages are at greater risk of dying from heart disease than non-smokers of the same age. The more cigarettes smoked, the more likely is death from heart disease.

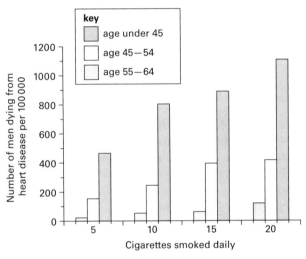

Smoking and the risk of dying from heart disease among men

Reducing risk

Do not smoke.

Diet and heart disease

People who eat too much fat and sugar tend to put on weight. Excessively overweight (**obese**) people have a higher risk of heart disease.

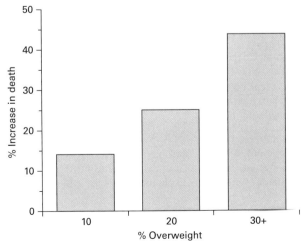

Increase in deaths from heart disease due to being overweight

11

Cholesterol is a clear, oily liquid often associated with heart disease. Large amounts of cholesterol are found in the deposits blocking blood vessels. Blocked blood vessels cause heart disease. The more cholesterol there is in the blood, the greater the risk of heart disease.

Eating food containing a lot of **saturated fat** seems to be the problem. Saturated fats raise the natural level of cholesterol in the blood.

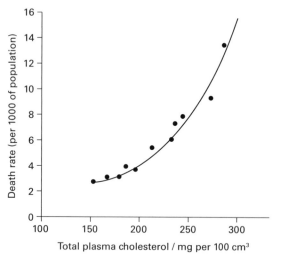

The relationship between blood cholesterol levels and risk of death from coronary heart disease

Cholesterol is insoluble and transported in the blood bound to **lipoprotein**. The proportions of **low density lipoproteins** (LDL) and **high density lipoproteins** (HDL) in the blood affect the risk of a person developing heart disease.

- Raised levels of **LDL** increase the risk of heart disease. It speeds up the formation of deposits blocking blood vessels.
- Raised levels of **HDL** lower the risk of heart disease. It removes cholesterol from the lining of the artery wall.

Reducing risk

An important first step to reducing levels of blood cholesterol is to change diet – increasing the intake of unsaturated fats at the expense of saturated fats. Different fats contain different proportions of saturated and unsaturated fatty acids.

How science works (E)

Association or cause and effect?

Diet is one of the most important factors affecting health. However, links between diet and health problems are not always clear cut. It is often difficult to pin down cause and effect. Rather, different dietary factors are **associated** with particular diseases.

For example, a high fat diet is associated with the development of heart disease. However, the evidence shows that we cannot be sure that it causes heart disease: only that it seems highly likely that this is the case.

Blood pressure and heart disease

Blood pressure results from the heart pumping blood into the blood vessels. It is measured in millimetres of mercury (mmHg) with an instrument called a **sphygmomanometer** or with a digital device that fits over the finger. Two readings are taken:

- **systolic blood pressure** – the pressure of blood when the heart contracts
- **diastolic blood pressure** – the pressure of blood when the heart relaxes

For a young adult, systolic pressure is about 120 mmHg and diastolic pressure about 75 mmHg. The pressures are written as 120/75.

Constant high blood pressure (**hypertension**) is harmful. It makes the heart work harder and causes the arteries to narrow because deposits within them build up more quickly. High blood pressure can also damage the kidneys and eyes, and increase the risk of rupture of an artery to the brain (**stroke** or **cerebral haemorrhage**).

Whether it is systolic pressure or diastolic pressure which is raised, the risk of heart disease is increased. For example, there is a 20% probability of death in middle age within five years if diastolic pressure is above 110 mmHg long term.

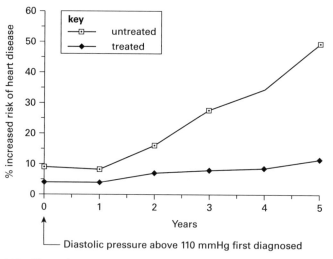

Risk of heart disease

Reducing risk

Different studies show that changes in lifestyle can have an important effect.

- **Salt** – reduction in salt intake reduces blood pressure.
- **Obesity** – losing 3 kg body weight typically reduces systolic blood pressure by 7 mmHg and diastolic blood pressure by 4 mmHg.
- **Smoking** – cigarette smokers, especially, are at risk of hypertension. Also, smokers respond less well to drugs designed to reduce hypertension. The message is **do not smoke**.

Stress and heart disease

The link between stress and heart disease is less obvious than the links with diet, smoking, and high blood pressure. However, worry, anxiety, or frequent crises increase levels of stress hormones like adrenaline in the blood. The hormones raise blood pressure and cholesterol levels increasing the risk of heart disease.

Reducing risk

Stress management helps. However, what is stressful to one person, is not to another. Judging stress is difficult and not an exact science. Some stress is a normal and healthy part of everyday life. It helps us keep alert and out of danger. It is when stress levels stay high for months or years that trouble starts and the heart may suffer.

Smoking and cancer

Unburnt tobacco contains at least 2500 chemicals. Of these, different forms of N-nitrosamines and metal compounds have been identified as **carcinogens** (substances which cause cancer).

Different **genes** control cell division so that it stops when enough cells have been produced. **Mutations** of the genes increase their activity, stimulating cell division.

- The mutated genes are called **oncogenes**, and cell division runs out of control. Cells proliferate and a cancer develops.
- The **ras** oncogenes account for 25% of cases of lung cancer. They are activated by the carcinogens in cigarette smoke.

Tobacco carcinogens may also lead to mutations of **tumour suppressor** genes which inhibit cell division.

- Loss or inactivation of these genes contributes to the loss of control over cell division and subsequent development of cancers – especially lung cancer.
- The tumour suppressor gene called **p53** is most often involved.

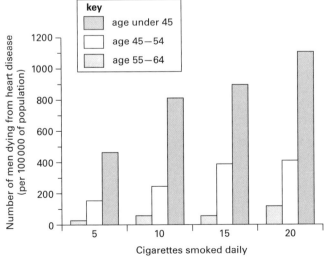

The risk of dying from lung cancer and the number of cigarettes smoked daily (men)

Non-smokers also suffer increased risks of ill health when they breathe in smoke from other people's cigarettes – so-called **passive smoking**. The evidence supports the idea that people have the right to a smoke-free environment. A change in UK law has made public transport and places where people work, shop, and find entertainment smoke-free zones.

Reducing risk

Do not smoke.

Sunlight and cancer

Malignant **melanoma** of the skin is a cancer which develops in the **melanocytes** (pigment-producing cells) in the skin. The disease is more common in fair-skinned people than in dark-skinned people. Overexposure to sunlight is a major risk factor.

Non-melanoma skin cancers are also caused by overexposure to sunlight.

Damage seems to be caused by the **ultraviolet (UV)** radiation part of the Sun's electromagnetic spectrum. UV radiation striking skin cells may damage the DNA in skin cell nuclei. Normally DNA repair systems in the cells swing into action and correct the damage. However, if DNA repair does not occur in melanocytes then abnormal DNA synthesis is the result and abnormal melanocytes develop.

Reducing risk

Wear clothes and hats that protect the body from direct sunlight. **Sunscreen** preparations smeared over bare skin also help. They reduce burning effects and may help prevent skin cancer by filtering UV radiation.

Questions

1 List unavoidable factors which affect the risk of someone developing coronary heart disease.
2 What are the different substances in cigarette smoke that cause cancer?
3 Explain how low density lipoproteins and high density lipoproteins affect the risk of a person developing heart disease.

1.03 The digestive system

OBJECTIVES

By the end of the section you should

○ *know that digestion is one of the processes which breaks down food as it passes through the digestive system*

○ *be able to identify different regions of the digestive system*

○ *know that digested food molecules are absorbed and assimilated to become tissues of the body*

The **gut** is an important part of the human digestive system. It is a muscular tube running from the mouth to the anus. In between the mouth and anus different processes break down food into substances suitable for absorption from the gut into the blood stream. One of the processes is digestion.

The sequence of processes including digestion is shown in the flow chart. Other parts of the human digestive system include the **liver, salivary glands,** and the **pancreas**.

The diagram shows the human digestive system, its position in the body, and a summary of the role of some of its parts in processing food.

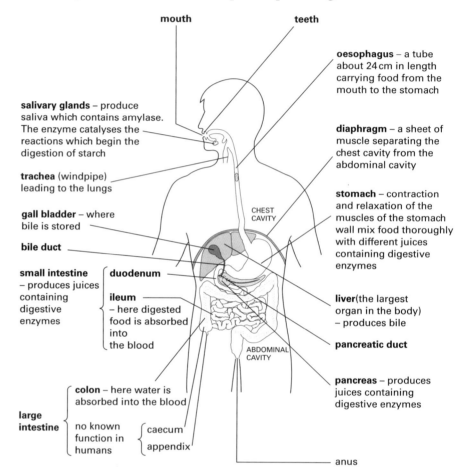

mouth   **teeth**

salivary glands – produce saliva which contains amylase. The enzyme catalyses the reactions which begin the digestion of starch

trachea (windpipe) leading to the lungs

gall bladder – where bile is stored

bile duct

small intestine – produces juices containing digestive enzymes

duodenum

ileum – here digested food is absorbed into the blood

large intestine

colon – here water is absorbed into the blood

no known function in humans

caecum

appendix

oesophagus – a tube about 24 cm in length carrying food from the mouth to the stomach

diaphragm – a sheet of muscle separating the chest cavity from the abdominal cavity

CHEST CAVITY

stomach – contraction and relaxation of the muscles of the stomach wall mix food thoroughly with different juices containing digestive enzymes

liver (the largest organ in the body) – produces bile

pancreatic duct

ABDOMINAL CAVITY

pancreas – produces juices containing digestive enzymes

anus

The human gut is 7–9 m long. The longest part of it consists of the **small intestine** and **large intestine**. These lie folded and packed into the space of the **abdominal cavity**. The small intestine is so called, not because of its length (it's more than 5 m long), but because its diameter is less than the large intestine. The liver, salivary glands, and pancreas are connected by ducts to the gut and play an important part in the digestion of food.

Ingestion

Food is taken into the mouth.

↓

Digestion

Substances consisting of large insoluble molecules which the body cannot absorb are broken down into small soluble molecules which the body can absorb.

↓

Absorption

The small molecules of digested food pass into the blood stream and are transported to the liver.

↓

Assimilation

Absorbed molecules become part of the tissues of the body.

Egestion

Undigested food and other wastes are removed from the body through the anus.

Questions

1 Identify some of the different parts of the human digestive system.

2 Why is the digestion of food necessary?

3 Explain the difference between the processes of ingestion and egestion.

1.04 Proteins

OBJECTIVES

By the end of the section you should

○ *be able to describe the general structure of an amino acid*

○ *understand the formation of peptide bonds*

○ *know that peptides and proteins are formed from amino acid molecules joined together*

○ *be able to explain the relationship between the primary structure, secondary structure, tertiary structure, and quaternary structure of proteins*

○ *be able to relate the structures of different proteins to their functions*

○ *be able to test for the presence of protein*

Before you start, it will help to read sections **1.06** (condensation reaction) and **1.10** (plasma membrane).

Amino acids – the building blocks of proteins

Proteins are compounds containing the elements carbon, hydrogen, oxygen, and nitrogen. Some also contain sulfur and phosphorus.

Amino acids are compounds which are the building blocks from which proteins are made. There are 20 different amino acids.

amino group $H_2N - \underset{\underset{H}{|}}{\overset{\overset{R \;\;\text{side group}}{|}}{C}} - COOH$ carboxyl group

The general structure of an amino acid

Each amino acid has a different R group. For example:

Amino acid	R group
glycine	$-H$
alanine	$-CH_3$
valine	$-CH(CH_2)_2$

There are 20 different R groups which is why there are 20 different amino acids.

Peptide bonds

A **dipeptide** is formed when two amino acid molecules combine.

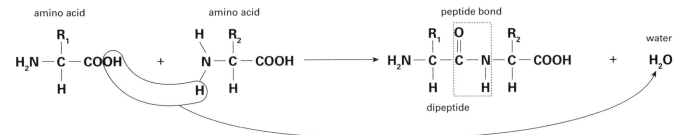

The structure of a dipeptide

Notice that
- the reaction is a **condensation** – the reverse **hydrolysis** would break the dipeptide into its component amino acid molecules
- the carboxyl group of one amino acid molecule reacts with the amino group of the other amino acid molecule – a molecule of water is eliminated
  ℝ As a result a **peptide bond** forms between the two amino acid molecules.
- the type of dipeptide formed depends on the structures of R_1 and R_2

The more amino acids joined together by condensation reactions, the larger is the resulting polymer.

Type of compound	Number of amino acid units joined together
dipeptide	2
peptide	3–20
polypeptide	21–50
protein	>50

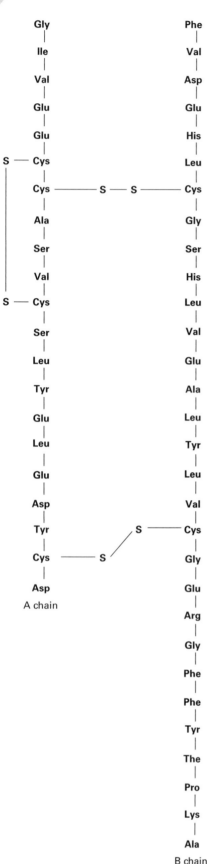

Gly
|
Ile
|
Val
|
Glu
|
Glu
|
S — Cys
|
Cys ——— S — S ——— Cys
|
Ala
|
Ser
|
Val
|
S — Cys
|
Ser
|
Leu
|
Tyr
|
Glu
|
Leu
|
Glu
|
Asp
|
Tyr   S
| /
Cys ——— S
|
Asp

A chain

Phe
|
Val
|
Asp
|
Glu
|
His
|
Leu
|
Cys
|
Gly
|
Ser
|
His
|
Leu
|
Val
|
Glu
|
Ala
|
Leu
|
Tyr
|
Leu
|
Val
|
Cys
|
Gly
|
Glu
|
Arg
|
Gly
|
Phe
|
Phe
|
Tyr
|
The
|
Pro
|
Lys
|
Ala

B chain

The primary structure of insulin

You do not need to learn this structure but it gives you an idea of the sequence.

Protein structure

Primary (1°) structure

The order in which one amino acid unit follows another in the polypeptide chain(s) is unique for each protein. This unique amino acid sequence dictates the structure, chemical properties, and function of the particular protein. The sequence of amino acid units is called the **primary (1°) structure** of the protein. The diagram shows the primary structure of the hormone insulin. Notice that

- the insulin molecule consists of two polypeptide chains joined together
- one end of each polypeptide chain ends in an $-NH_3^+$ group (the amino end)
- the other end of each polypeptide chain ends in a $-COO^-$ group (the carboxyl end)

Secondary, **tertiary**, and **quaternary** structures of proteins arise from the primary structure of polypeptides.

The primary structure of a polypeptide chain allows

- hydrogen bonds to form between different amino acids along the chain
- interactions between R groups of the amino acids along the chain

  Ⓡ As a result the polypeptide chain bends and twists giving rise to the secondary, tertiary, and quaternary structures that shape the protein molecule.

Secondary (2°) structure

Secondary structure arises because of hydrogen bonding between the oxygen of the >C=O group of one amino acid unit and the hydrogen of the >NH group of another amino acid unit.

- If this bonding occurs within one polypeptide chain, the chain coils into an alpha helix (α-**helix**).
- If this bonding occurs between different, parallel polypeptide chains, the chains fold into a beta pleated sheet (β-**pleated sheet**).

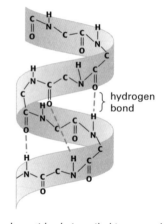

A polypeptide chain coiled into an α-helix

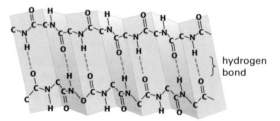

A polypeptide chain forming a β-pleated sheet

Tertiary (3°) structure

Tertiary structure arises when the α-helices and β-pleated sheets of many proteins fold and coil into a shape which is held in place by chemical bonds between different groups in the polypeptide chain.

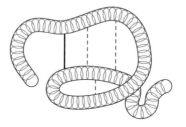

key

| = strong bond

¦ = weak bond

Different bonds hold together the tertiary structure of a protein

The chemical bonds between some of the groups are weak. This means that the shape of the tertiary structure of proteins is flexible – it can be altered by changes in physical conditions (e.g. pH, temperature). The alterations are reversible and allow the molecules to carry out their different functions.

Quaternary (4°) structure

Quaternary structure arises when a protein molecule consists of two or more polypeptide chains. Haemoglobin (the oxygen carrying pigment in red blood cells) is an example. The way in which the chains fit together is maintained by the same types of chemical bond that hold together its tertiary structures.

Functions of proteins

The structure of proteins is a clue to their function in organisms.

Fibrous proteins consist of long polypeptide chains which run parallel to one another. Their function in cells and organisms is usually structural. **Collagen** is an example. Its fibres are insoluble, inelastic, and have high tensile strength. This makes collagen an ideal material for **tendons** and ligaments which must withstand large pulling forces.

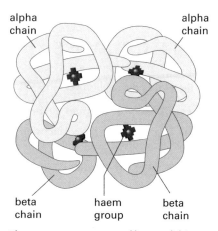

The quaternary structure of haemoglobin. Each alpha (α) and beta (β) polypeptide chain consists of about 140 amino acids.

> ### Fact file
>
> About 25% of the protein that makes the human body is collagen. It is a component of skin, teeth, bone, cartilage, and blood vessels as well as tendons and ligaments.

Globular proteins consist of polypeptide chains that fold up into a spherical shape. The environment inside cells and organisms is aqueous. The folding of globular proteins places the

- hydrophobic side chains in the interior of the molecule
- hydrophilic side chains on the outside of the molecule

  - As a result water molecules are excluded from the hydrophobic centre of the folded protein molecule but gather around the hydrophilic surface.
  - As a result globular proteins are usually soluble.

Enzymes, antibodies, and some hormones are globulins. Haemoglobin is another.

Testing for protein

Adding an alkaline solution of copper(II) sulfate to material that contains peptides or proteins produces a **pink to purple** colour. The test is called the **biuret** test. It detects peptide bonds. All peptides and proteins, therefore, give a positive result.

The biuret test is a **qualitative** test but can also be used semi-quantitatively. The colours produced depend on the number of peptide bonds in the test substance. Their range is:

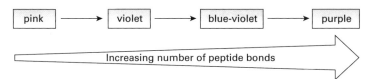

Proteins give a characteristic purple colour with the biuret test because the components contain the most peptide bonds per molecule.

Questions

1 Which elements make up a molecule of amino acid?
2 What is the primary structure of a protein?
3 What type of chemical reaction forms peptide bonds?
4 Briefly describe the buiret test for proteins.

1.05 Enzymes

OBJECTIVES

By the end of the section you should

○ *know that most enzymes are proteins*

○ *be able to explain the relationship between enzymes and activation energy*

○ *understand the mechanism of enzyme action*

○ *be able to explain that different factors affect the rate of enzyme activity*

Before you start, it will help to read section **1.04** (protein structure) and **1.07** (amylase and the carbohydrases).

Most enzymes are globular proteins. They are **catalysts**. In general, a catalyst

• alters the rate of a chemical reaction

• is effective in small amounts

• is involved in but unchanged by the chemical reaction it catalyses

All the features of catalysts are also features of enzymes. In addition enzymes are

• specific in their action, catalysing a particular chemical reaction or type of reaction

• sensitive to changes in pH and temperature

Remember

• The substance an enzyme helps to react is the **substrate**.

• The substance formed by the reaction is the **product**.

• When an enzyme and its substrate bind together an **enzyme–substrate complex** is formed.

Only a small part of an enzyme molecule binds with its substrate molecule. The part is called the **active site**. It consists of just a few of the amino acid units that make up the enzyme molecule as a whole.

Enzymes lower activation energy

Activation energy is the amount of energy required to bring about any particular chemical reaction. Without it chemical reactions will not take place.

Enzymes lower activation energy by forming **enzyme–substrate** complexes. They enable reactions which would need high temperatures in the laboratory to take place at body temperature.

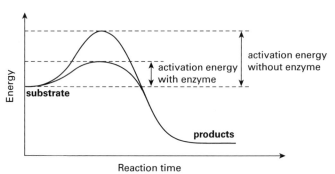

How do enzymes work?

The shape of an enzyme, like all proteins, is the result of its tertiary structure. An enzyme's active site also has a precise shape. An enzyme will bind with a particular substrate molecule because the shape of the active site is **complementary** to (opposite to) the shape of the substrate molecule. The two shapes fit like a key fits into a lock.

The idea of **lock and key** helps to explain why a particular enzyme will only catalyse a particular chemical reaction (or type of reaction). Only the shape of the substrate molecule in question fits the active site of the enzyme. The diagram shows an example of this.

substrate (part of a starch molecule) — hydrolysis — H_2O — products (maltose molecules)

active site

amylase molecule (enzyme) — enzyme substrate complex — amylase molecule unchanged

The enzyme amylase binds with starch, catalysing the breaking of alternate glycosidic bonds. The reactions are hydrolyses and maltose is formed.

How science works (A)

'Lock and key' suggests that the active site of an enzyme and its substrate are *exactly* complementary. Recent work favours the **induced fit hypothesis**:

• The active site and substrate are fully complementary only *after* binding has taken place.

• The initial binding of a substrate molecule to the active site alters the shape (tertiary structure) of the active site.

As a result the shape of the substrate molecule then alters, assisting the reaction to take place.

Factors affecting the activity of enzymes

Remember that any factor that affects the shape of an enzyme molecule, in particular its active site, affects the activity of the enzyme.

Temperature

In general, the rate of chemical reactions increases with temperature (doubles for every 10 °C rise in temperature). But for enzyme-catalysed reactions, this is true only within a limited range of temperature. Once an enzyme reaches its optimum, any further increase in temperature causes a decrease in the rate of reaction. (See the graph on the facing page.)

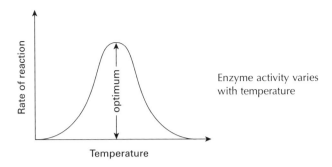

Enzyme activity varies with temperature

The decrease is caused by a permanent change in the shape of the enzyme (and its active site). We say that the enzyme is **denatured**. Its active site is no longer complementary with the substrate molecule.

Qs and As

Q What does 'optimum' mean when we talk about the effect of temperature on enzyme activity?

A *The 'optimum' is the temperature value at which the number of collisions between an active enzyme and its substrate is at a maximum. As a result the rate of the enzyme-catalysed reaction is at a maximum.*

---

pH

A change of pH from the optimum for a particular enzyme alters the electric charge carried by the amino acid units forming the active site. The enzyme (and its active site) is denatured, and is no longer complementary with the substrate molecule. This causes a decrease in the rate of reaction.

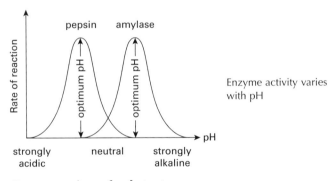

Enzyme activity varies with pH

Concentration of substrate

An increase in the concentration of substrate affects the rate of reaction for a fixed concentration of enzyme.

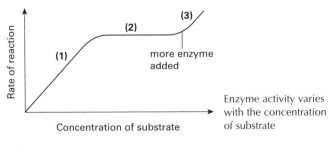

Enzyme activity varies with the concentration of substrate

Notice that

- if there is an excess of enzyme, the rate of reaction is directly proportional to the concentration of the substrate **(1)**

- when all the enzyme active sites are occupied by substrate molecules the rate of reaction is limited **(2)**
- addition of more enzyme results in an increase in the rate of reaction which is proportional to the concentration of the substrate **(3)**

The effects of substrate concentration on the rate of reaction assume that all the other conditions that affect the rate of enzyme-catalysed reactions (e.g. pH, temperature) are constant.

Enzyme inhibition

Substances which *reduce* the rate of reaction when added to an enzyme/substrate mixture are called **inhibitors**.

Competitive inhibition

A **competitive inhibitor** is a substance that combines with the active site of an enzyme, preventing its normal substrate from binding with it. The diagram shows you the idea.

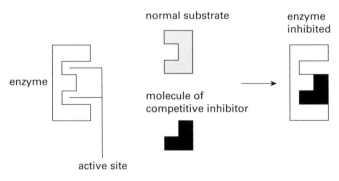

Enzyme inhibition

Non-competitive inhibition

A **non-competitive inhibitor** is a substance that combines with some part of an enzyme molecule *other* than its active site. The change in the shape of the enzyme molecule causes a change in the shape of its active site. The substrate molecule is no longer able to bind to the active site.

The inhibition may be

- **reversible** – breaking up the inhibitor–enzyme complex *is* possible
- **irreversible** – breaking up the inhibitor–enzyme complex *is not* possible. Heavy metals such as arsenic (As) and mercury (Hg) are irreversible non-competitive inhibitors.

Allosteric inhibition

In some enzymes, a chemical group other than the active site can bind with a substance other than the normal substrate. The group is called the **allosteric site**. An **allosteric inhibitor** is a substance which reversibly combines with the allosteric site.

Questions

1 What is activation energy and how do enzymes affect it?

2 Use the induced fit hypothesis to describe the binding of an enzyme with its substrate.

3 Why does denaturation affect the activity of an enzyme?

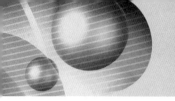

1.06 Carbohydrates

OBJECTIVES

By the end of the section you should

○ *know the formulae of a variety of carbohydrates*

○ *understand the formation of glycosidic bonds*

○ *know that disaccharides and polysaccharides are made from monosaccharides joined together*

○ *know how to test for the presence of sugars and starch*

Before you start, it will help to read sections **1.07** (digestion of maltose) and **1.10** (plasma membrane).

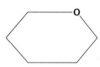

The structural formula of α-glucose. The numbers show the positions of the carbon atoms in the molecule.

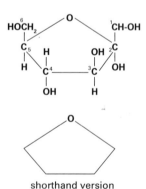

The structural formula of fructose. The numbers show the positions of the carbon atoms in the molecule.

Carbohydrates are compounds containing the elements carbon, hydrogen, and oxygen only. There are three main categories:

- **Monosaccharides** – single sugars. **Glucose** and **fructose** are examples. They are the basic molecular units (**monomers**) of which carbohydrates are made.
- **Disaccharides** – double sugars. **Maltose**, **sucrose**, and **lactose** are examples. One molecule of a disaccharide is formed when two monosaccharide molecules combine.
- **Polysaccharides** – compounds which are formed from the combination of hundreds of monosaccharide molecules. **Starch**, **glycogen**, and **cellulose** are examples.

Monosaccharides

In general the **molecular** formula of monosaccharides is written as $(CH_2O)n$. Some examples are given in the table. Notice that the ratio of hydrogen and oxygen atoms is 2:1 – the same as water. The term carbohydrate means 'hydrated carbon'.

Value of n	Type of monosaccharide	Molecular formula	Examples
3	trioses	$C_3H_6O_3$	glyceraldehyde
5	pentoses	$C_5H_{10}O_5$	ribose
6	hexoses	$C_6H_{12}O_6$	glucose, fructose

Notice that glucose and fructose have the same molecular formula because they consist of the same atoms in the same proportions. However, their **structural** formulae show how the arrangement of the atoms of each molecule is different. We say that glucose and fructose are structural **isomers**.

Glucose molecules exist in two forms (**isomers**): (alpha) α-glucose and (beta) β-glucose. The diagram on the left shows α-glucose. If you imagine the molecules as 3D structures, with the hexagonal ring like a flat plate, the hydroxyl group (–OH) on carbon atom 1 is

- below the plane of the ring in α-glucose
- above the plane of the ring in β-glucose

Using 'shorthand' forms of molecules makes it easier to understand the structural changes taking place during chemical reactions.

Dissacharides

A **disaccharide** is formed when two monosaccharide molecules combine. For example, the diagram below shows how two molecules of α-glucose combine to form one molecule of **maltose**.

The formation of maltose

Notice that

- the reaction is a **condensation**. (The reverse **hydrolysis** breaks down maltose into its component α-glucose molecules.)
- the formation of a water molecule results in an oxygen 'bridge' joining the two molecules. The link is called a **glycosidic bond**.

In maltose the glycosidic bond is between carbon atoms 1 and 4 of the adjacent α-glucose units. However, different disaccharides are produced if
- the combination of monosaccharide molecules is different and
- the links between carbon atoms in adjacent monosaccharide molecules is different

For example:
- **sucrose** = α-glucose + β-fructose
- **lactose** = α-glucose + galactose

Polysaccharides

Polysaccharides are formed from many monosaccharide molecules joined by condensation reactions. Their general formula is:

$$nC_6H_{12}O_6 \rightarrow (C_6H_{10}O_5)n + nH_2O \qquad \text{where } n = 10^2 \rightarrow 10^3$$

For example, **starch** is made from many condensation reactions forming glycosidic bonds between α-glucose molecules.

Testing for sugars

All monosaccharides (e.g. glucose and fructose) and some disaccharides (e.g. maltose and lactose, but not sucrose) are **reducing sugars**. They contain a free **aldehyde** group ($-CHO$) or **ketone** group ($>C=O$) which reduces copper(II) ions (Cu^{2+}) to copper(I) ions (Cu^+) when heated in an alkaline solution. This is the basis of the **Benedict's test** for reducing sugars.
- Benedict's reagent turns from blue to red when heated with a reducing sugar.

Testing for non-reducing sugars

Sucrose is an example of a **non-reducing sugar**. It does not give a positive result to a simple Benedict's test. However, if sucrose solution is first heated with dilute hydrochloric acid then it hydrolyses into its component monosaccharide molecules. These then test positive when heated with Benedict's reagent. This is the basis of the test for a non-reducing sugar.
- The sugar solution gives a negative result when heated with Benedict's solution (no colour change).
- When hydrolysed (by heating with acid) and then neutralized (by adding sodium hydrogencarbonate), testing again gives a positive result to the Benedict's test (changes from blue to red).

Testing for starch

Starch doesn't dissolve in water but forms a suspension. Iodine doesn't dissolve in water either, but does dissolve in potassium iodide solution. When this iodine solution is added to the starch suspension, it turns from yellow-orange to an intense blue-black. This is the basis of the **iodine test** for starch.
- Starch turns iodine solution blue-black.

Questions

1 The term 'carbohydrate' means hydrated carbon. Explain the link between the term and the general formula for a monosaccharide.

2 Why are molecules of glucose and fructose described as structural isomers?

3 Briefly describe a test which identifies the presence of non-reducing sugars.

OBJECTIVES

By the end of the section you should

○ *know that carbohydrate digestion begins in the mouth*

○ *understand the role of carbohydrates in carbohydrate digestion*

○ *know that the later stages of carbohydrate digestion are intracellular*

Before you start, it will help to read sections **1.03** (digestion), **1.05** (enzymes), **1.06** (carbohydrates), and **1.10** (plasma membrane checklist 2).

Our **diet** is the food we eat and drink. The carbohydrates in our diet are mostly in the form of complex *insoluble* molecules like starch, which the body cannot absorb. The processes of **digestion** break down these insoluble molecules into their *soluble* component sugar molecules, which the body can absorb. Breakdown occurs by **hydrolysis**.

Remember that glycosidic bonds join monosaccharides together, forming polysaccharides. Different enzymes catalyse the hydrolytic reactions which break these bonds during carbohydrate digestion.

The different enzymes which catalyse the reactions of carbohydrate digestion are called **carbohydrases**. Amylase is a particular carbohydrase which catalyses the hydrolysis of starch, forming maltose.

The action of amylase

In humans the digestion of food begins in the mouth. The teeth break up food (chewing), increasing the surface area exposed to the action of digestive enzymes. Saliva, produced from three pairs of salivary glands in the head, pours onto the food in the mouth. Saliva contains

- **salivary amylase**, the carbohydrase which catalyses the hydrolysis of starch (polysaccharide) to maltose (disaccharide)
- chloride ions (Cl^-) which activate amylase

The action of amylase on starch. Notice that the enzyme catalyses the hydrolysis of the α-1-4 glycosidic bonds between alternate α-glucose units.

Pancreatic juice, produced by some of the tissues of the pancreas, passes from the pancreas through the pancreatic duct into the duodenum. The juice contains amylase, which continues to catalyse the digestion of starch begun in the mouth by salivary amylase.

Carbohydrases produced in the intestinal epithelium

Most of the enzymes found in the small intestine come from the pancreas. The enzymes secreted from the intestinal wall itself are produced within the epithelial cells of the intestinal wall. The enzyme content of the cells increases as they mature and pass to the tops of the villi. When the cells are dislodged from the villi their disintegration releases the enzymes within, adding to the digestive enzymes already at work.

The action of maltase on maltose

The carbohydrases include:

- **maltase** which catalyses the hydrolysis of maltose to glucose
- **sucrase** which catalyses the hydrolysis of sucrose to glucose and fructose
- **lactase** which catalyses the hydrolysis of lactose to glucose and galactose. The absence of lactase is the cause of **lactose intolerance** in affected individuals.

The later stages of carbohydrate digestion occur on or within the cells of the intestinal epithelium. Digestion taking place within the cells is called **intracellular** digestion.

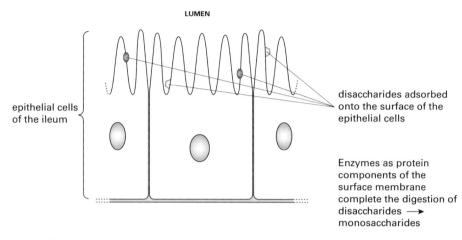

LUMEN

epithelial cells of the ileum

disaccharides adsorbed onto the surface of the epithelial cells

Enzymes as protein components of the surface membrane complete the digestion of disaccharides ⟶ monosaccharides

Carbohydrases in the lumen of the gut catalyse the conversion of most carbohydrates to disaccharides and some monosaccharides

Conclusion: making the link

An overview of the sequence of the processes of carbohydrate digestion is summarized in the table. It will help you make links between the processes.

Region of the gut	Digestive juice	Source of the digestive juice	pH of the region of the gut	Digestive enzyme	Substrate	Product
mouth	saliva	salivary glands	6.5–7.5	amylase	starch	maltose
duodenum	pancreatic juice	exocrine tissue of the pancreas	7.0	amylase	starch	maltose
ileum		epithelial cells of the intestinal wall	8.5	maltase sucrase lactase	maltose sucrose lactose	glucose glucose and fructose glucose and galactose

---

Questions

1 What is the difference between a carbohydrase and the enzyme amylase?

2 What causes lactose intolerance?

3 In each case name the monosaccharides which result from the digestion of maltose, sucrose, and lactose.

1.08 Investigating cells

OBJECTIVES

By the end of the section you should

○ be able to explain the relationship between magnification and the resolving power of a microscope

○ understand the principles and limitations of transmission and scanning electron microscopes

○ be able to explain the techniques of fractionation and centrifugation

Before you start, it will help to read section **1.09** (cell structure).

Seeing cells

Most cells are too small to be seen with the unaided eye. Different types of microscope help us look at cells.

The transmission electron microscope (TEM) reveals the structure of cells in more detail than the optical (light) microscope. The level of detail seen (**resolution** of the image) is a measure of the **resolving power** of the microscope.

- The resolving power of a microscope is its ability to distinguish between structures lying close together.

- Magnifying structures to the limits of a microscope's resolving power reveals more and more detail. But structures lying closer together than the ability of the microscope to resolve them appear as a single structure.

  - As a result, magnifying structures beyond a microscope's resolving power enlarges the image but does not improve clarity of detail.

- The limit of resolution is *one half* the wavelength of the electromagnetic radiation (light or electrons) used to illuminate the specimen under observation.

Magnification is useful when it clarifies the details of a specimen. It is not useful when the limitations of the resolving power of the microscope begin to blur the details. Useful magnification depends on the wavelength of the electromagnetic radiation used to illuminate the specimen.

Property	Light microscope	TEM
wavelength	400–700 nm	0.005 nm
resolving power	200 nm	0.5 nm (technical difficulties reduce resolution of the image compared with the theoretical best value)
maximum useful magnification	× 2000	× 2 000 000

Electron microscopes

The transmission electron microscope (TEM)

In the TEM a beam of electrons passes *through* the specimen under observation. More electrons pass through some parts of the specimen than others. The electrons then hit a screen coated with phosphorescent material which glows on their impact. The more electron hits, the brighter the glow. The image produced is a highly detailed shadow of the specimen.

The scanning electron microscope (SEM)

In the SEM a beam of electrons *scans* (moves over) the specimen and knocks electrons loose from the specimen's surface. These electrons are captured and a computer processes the information, assembling a detailed three-dimensional image of the specimen's surface features. The depth of field of view in the SEM is much greater than in the TEM. However its maximum magnification is one order of magnitude (×10) less than the TEM.

Advantages and limitations

High magnification without loss of resolution (the detailed structures of specimens remain clear) is an important advantage of the different types of electron microscope compared with optical microscopes. However, limitations include

- the expense of buying the instruments, using them and maintaining them
- the difficulty of preparing specimens free of artefacts (features seen in preparations of cells which are not present in living cells)
- their sensitivity to magnetic fields

> ## Qs and As
>
> **Q** Why is it necessary to have a vacuum inside the body of an electron microscope?
>
> **A** *Electrons are deflected when they strike molecules of the gases which make up air, making it difficult to focus the electron beam. Producing a vacuum within the microscope solves the problem.*

Fractionation and centrifugation

- **Fractionation** (breaking up cells suspended in liquid) releases the structures within cells.
- **Centrifugation** involves spinning test tubes, each containing a suspension of **organelles** (cell structures), in a centrifuge at high speed. This separates the different organelles.

The flow chart summarizes the techniques. All stages take place in chilled conditions to reduce self-digestion of organelles.

Fractionation

Fragments of tissue are homogenized (broken up) using a pestle homogenizer, blender, or sonification (high frequency sound).

Suspension of organelles

Centrifugation

Test tubes holding a suspension of organelles are spun at high speed.

The faster the spin speed, the greater is the force in excess of normal gravity (g force) exerted on the contents of the tube.

The distance organelles move in the suspension depends on the
- mass, density, and shape of each organelle
- mass, density, and viscosity (fluidity) of the liquid in which the organelles are suspended

Differential centrifugation

The suspension of organelles is spun at different speeds for a given amount of time at each speed.

Organelles having the greatest density spin down first at slow speed (less g force) towards the bottom of the tube.

Less dense organelles spin down at higher speeds (greater g force).

Centrifugation at
- 700 g for 20 minutes spins down nuclei and chloroplasts
- 20 000 g for 20 minutes spins down mirochondria and lysosomes
- 100 000 g (ultracentrifugation) for 60 minutes spins down ribosomes and fragments of the endoplasmic reticulum

OR

Density-gradient centrifugation

The suspension of organelles is added to a sucrose solution which is
- least dense near the top of the test tube and
- most dense at the bottom of the test tube.

There is a continous density gradient of sucrose in between the top and bottom of the column of liquid.

As the centrifuge spins at an appropriate speed, organelles having the greatest density move towards the bottom of the tube.

Other organelles form layers above them, each in a position where the density of the organelle matches the density of the sucrose solution.

The organelles are removed through an opening in the bottom of the plastic tets tube, layer by layer in the order 1 ⟶ 4

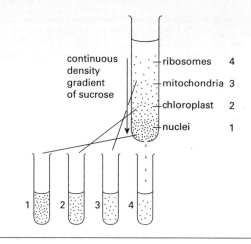

The different techniques of centrifugation provide pure samples of organelles. Each type of organelle can then be analysed separately. This means that the outcome of the analysis will not be affected by other types of organelle.

Questions

1 Explain the difference between the magnifying power and the resolving power of a microscope.

2 Why is the resolving power of a transmission electron microscope greater than that of an optical microscope?

3 Explain why centrifugation can provide pure samples of organelles.

OBJECTIVES

By the end of the section you should

○ *know the structure of an epithelial cell from the small intestine as seen with an optical microscope*

○ *know the appearance, ultrastructure, and function of different parts of a eukaryotic cell*

○ *be able to explain the adaptation of different cells*

Before you start, it will help to read section **1.08** (types of microscope).

Cell structure

The optical microscope shows that epithelial cells from the intestine are each a unit of **protoplasm** surrounded by a **plasma membrane**. The protoplasm consists of **cytoplasm** in which is embedded a spherical **nucleus**. Notice that the cytoplasm appears speckled.

The resolving power of a transmission electron microscope (TEM) shows the details of **organelles** and other structures not seen even with the best optical microscope.

cytoplasm – where most of the chemical reactions occurring in the cell take place

plasma membrane – surrounds the cell and controls the passage of substances in and out of it.

mitochondria – where most energy is released in cellular respiration

nucleus – controls the activities of the cell

A representation of epithelial cells as seen through an optical microscope

endoplasmic reticulum – a network of channels running through the cytoplasm from the nucleus to the surface of the cell. Substances are transported throughout the cell by the endoplasmic reticulum.

ribosomes – bead-like structures on the endoplasmic reticulum and in the cytoplasm. Proteins are made on the ribosomes.

glycogen granule

cytoplasm – a solution of different substances through which runs the cytoskeleton, giving support and shape to the cell

lysosomes – sac-like structures which contain high levels of digestive enzymes which would destroy the cell if released into the cytoplasm. The alkaline environment within lysosomes inactivates the enzymes. Lysosomes are abundant in cells like phagocytes.

microvilli – extensions of the plasma membrane increasing the surface area of the cell, maximizing the rate of absorption of substances across the plasma membrane

plasma membrane

nucleus containing threads of chromatin (made of DNA and protein)

nuclear membrane

pore in nuclear membrane

mitochondrion – where energy is released as the result of the reactions of aerobic respiration

Golgi apparatus – a stack of sac-like structures which package different substances (e.g. carbohydrates and proteins forming glycoproteins). Vesicles bud off, filled with packaged substances. They pass to the plasma membrane where the substances are secreted (released from the cell).

A representation of an epithelial cell as seen through a TEM

Fact file

The term **eukaryotic** refers to cells which each have a distinct nucleus. The cells of plants, animals, fungi, and protists (single-celled organisms) are eukaryotic.

Organelles are compartments within the cell bounded by membranes which separate the **organelles** one from another. Compartmentalization within a cell allows activities which would otherwise interfere with one another to take place at the same time.

Cells are specialized

The human body is made up of more than 200 different types of cell. Each type of cell is adapted enabling it to carry out a particular task (the cell's function).

Questions

1 Explain the importance of compartmentalization in cells.

2 Describe the role of the following in cells:

   a ribosomes

   b mitochondria

   c endoplasmic reticulum

   d Golgi apparatus

Ciliated cells line the windpipe. Their cilia sweep away a covering layer of mucus.

Skin cells cover the body.

Muscle cells form muscles which shorten and lengthen.

White blood cells help defend the body against disease.

Red blood cells absorb oxygen. The cell does not have a nucleus.

Sperm – the male sex cell. Each one has a long tail which lashes from side-to-side propelling the sperm to the egg.

Examples of specialized cells in the human body

1.10 Lipids, phospholipids, and the plasma membrane

OBJECTIVES

By the end of the section you should

○ *understand that triglycerides are made by the combination of three fatty acid molecules with one molecule of glycerol*

○ *know the meaning of the words 'saturation' and 'unsaturation'*

○ *understand the role of phospholipids, cholesterol, glycolipids, proteins, and glycoproteins as components of the plasma membrane*

Before you start, it will help to read sections **1.04** (protein structure), **1.18** (antigens), and **2.22** (protein pumps).

Remember that the valency of a carbon atom is 4.

Lipids

Lipids are compounds containing the elements carbon, hydrogen, and oxygen only. **Fats** and **oils** produced by plants and animals are lipids – fats are solid at room temperature, oils are liquid at room temperature.

Most lipids are mixtures of **triglycerides**.

- A triglyceride is an ester of fatty acids and glycerol (an ester is a substance formed from the reaction between an acid and an alcohol).
- A molecule of fatty acid consists of a hydrocarbon chain and a carboxyl group ($-COOH$). The table gives examples.

Fatty acid	Molecular formula
stearic acid	$C_{17}H_{35}COOH$
oleic acid	$C_{17}H_{33}COOH$
palmitic acid	$C_{15}H_{31}COOH$

The formula of glycerol is:

$$CH_2-OH$$
$$|$$
$$CH-OH$$
$$|$$
$$CH_2-OH$$

Molecules of fatty acid and glycerol combine to form a triglyceride like this:

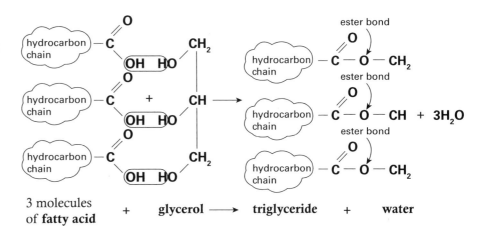

| 3 molecules of **fatty acid** | + | **glycerol** | → | **triglyceride** | + | **water** |

Notice that

- the combination of molecules of fatty acid with the molecule of glycerol is a condensation reaction
- three molecules of fatty acid are combined with one molecule of glycerol producing a triglyceride and a molecule of water
  - a **simple** triglyceride is formed if the fatty acid molecules are the same
  - a **mixed** triglyceride is formed if the fatty acid molecules are different

Saturation and unsaturation

Saturated – all the bonds linking adjacent carbon atoms of the hydrocarbon chain of the fatty acid are single bonds:

$$CH_3-CH_2-CH_2-CH_2-CH_2-CH_2-CH_2-CH_2-$$

Monounsaturated – the hydrocarbon chain of the fatty acid contains one double bond:

$$CH_3-CH_2-CH=CH-CH_2-CH_2-CH_2-CH_2-$$

Polyunsaturated – the hydrocarbon chain of the fatty acid contains more than one double bond:

$$CH_3-CH_2-CH=CH-CH_2-CH=CH-CII_2-$$

- Saturated fatty acids combine with glycerol to form saturated triglycerides.
- Unsaturated fatty acids combine with glycerol to form unsaturated triglycerides.

The emulsion test for lipids

Different tests may be used to detect the presence of lipids. One of them is the **emulsion test**:

- Mix ethanol and the test material in equal volumes. Shake to help dissolve any lipids present.
- Then add an equal volume of water and shake the mixture again. A milky white emulsion indicates the presence of lipids.

Phospholipids

Phospholipids are triglycerides which contain a phosphate group instead of one of the fatty acid components.

- The phosphate group dissolves in water and is therefore **hydrophilic** (literally 'water loving').
- The hydrocarbon chains of the two fatty acid components do not dissolve in water and are therefore **hydrophobic** (literally 'water hating').

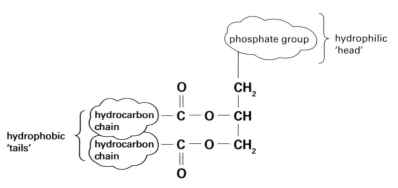

The structure and function of cell membranes depend on the hydrophilic and hydrophobic properties of phospholipid molecules.

The plasma membrane

Cells are each surrounded by a **plasma membrane**. The diagrams with their checklists are your guide to the structure and function of the plasma membrane.

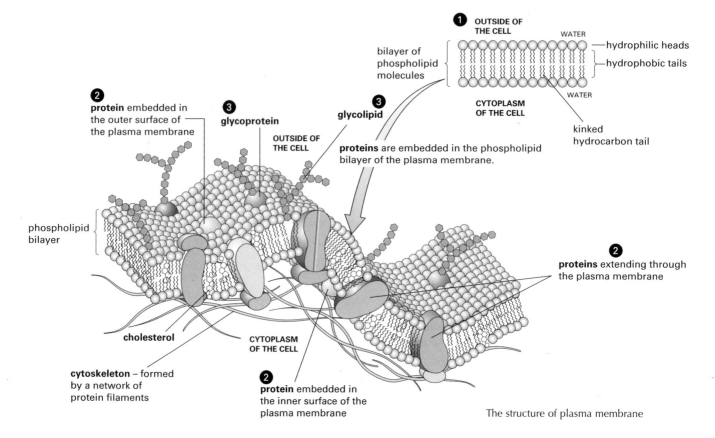

The structure of plasma membrane

Checklist ❶

- **Phosopholipids** are an important part of the plasma membrane. Remember that they have hydrophilic heads (phosphate groups) and hydrophobic tails (hydrocarbon chains). Remember also that cells are aqueous within and bathed in water without.
  - As a result, in water phospholipid molecules spontaneously form a stable two layer framework called a phospholipid **bilayer**. The hydrophobic tails point inwards, shielded from the water. The hydrophilic heads face outwards, forming hydrogen bonds with the water.
- The hydrocarbon tails of many of the phospholipid molecules are 'kinked' because of the presence of double bonds.
  - As a result phospholipids are loosely packed together.
  - As a result the plasma membrane is fluid.
  - As a result proteins and other material can move sideways within the membrane.
- Cholesterol is a lipid. Its molecules, wedged into the bilayer, help to keep the plasma membrane fluid at low temperatures.

Checklist ❷

- Different **proteins** are embedded in the phospholipid bilayer.
- Some proteins extend through the membrane; others are localized on one side of the membrane or the other.

The different proteins perform many of the functions of the plasma membrane. Functions include:

- action as enzymes – for example, enzymes on the surfaces of cells lining the intestine catalyse the reactions which digest food
- transport of substances across the membrane
- maintenance of cell shape
- formation of structures which stick cells together
- binding of messenger molecules. The proteins to which messenger molecules bind are called **receptors**. The messenger molecules trigger particular activities in the cell.

Checklist ❸

- Sugars bond to proteins and lipids embedded in the outside surface of the plasma membrane.
- A combination of a carbohydrate and a protein forms a **glycoprotein**. A combination of a carbohydrate and a lipid forms a **glycolipid**.
- Glycolipids are receptors for chemicals that are signals between cells. Cells therefore recognize other cells. Glycoproteins work in a similar way.
- Glycoproteins also enable cells of the immune system to recognize foreign cells such as bacteria, which may cause disease.
- Glycolipids and glycoproteins vary from species to species and from one individual to another of the same species. They are identification tags on the surface of cells and unique to the individual.

Fact file

Membranes are often described as a **fluid mosaic**.

- Their fluidity arises from the loose packing of the molecules of the phospholipid bilayer – this allows sideways movements of proteins and other materials.
- The word 'mosaic' describes the scattering of the different protein molecules embedded within the phospholipid bilayer.

Questions

1. Describe how you would use a biochemical test to show that a food contained lipids.
2. Explain why the plasma membrane of a cell is described as a fluid mosaic.
3. The diagram represents a molecule of phospholipids. Identify the components **x, y, z**.

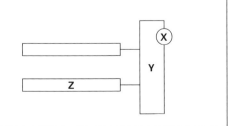

1.11 Diffusion, osmosis, and active transport

OBJECTIVES

By the end of the section you should

○ *know that there is constant movement of molecules and ions into and out of cells, and inside cells*

○ *understand the processes of diffusion, osmosis, and active transport*

○ *be able to explain the effects on cells of immersing them in solutions of different water potential*

Before you start, it will help to read sections **1.04** (structure of proteins) and **1.10** (plasma membrane).

Fact file

Cell membranes allow some molecules and ions to pass *freely* across but *restrict* the passage of others. We say that the membranes are **partially permeable**.

Diffusion

Diffusion is the net movement of a substance through a gas or solution from a region where the substance is in high concentration to a region where it is in low concentration. Diffusion continues until the concentration of the substance is the same throughout the gas or solution.

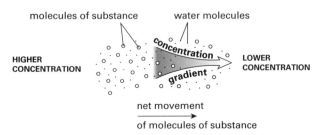

Diffusion

Different factors affect the rate of diffusion:

• The **concentration gradient** of a substance is the difference in concentration between the regions through which the substance is diffusing, divided by the distance.

• The bigger the difference between regions of high concentration and low concentration of a substance, the bigger the concentration gradient.

  ☞ As a result the rate of diffusion is maximized.

• The rate of diffusion of a substance decreases in proportion to the square of the distance over which diffusion is taking place (rate $\propto 1/\text{distance}^2$).

  ☞ As a result diffusion is only effective as a mechanism for the transport of substances over very short distances.

  ☞ As a result membranes are thin.

  ☞ As a result the size of cells is limited because diffusion is an important mechanism for the transport of substances across membranes within cells.

• The greater the **surface area** of a membrane, the greater is the rate of diffusion of substance through it.

The different factors are summarized by **Fick's law** as:

$$\text{rate of diffusion} \propto \frac{\text{surface area} \times \text{concentration difference}}{\substack{\text{distance of concentration gradient} \\ \text{(length of diffusion path)}}}$$

Qs and As

Q Molecules move as a result of their kinetic energy. Their movement is random. In other words there is an equal probability of any one molecule moving in any one of a complete range of directions. Why, therefore, do molecules move down a concentration gradient?

A *If molecules are more highly concentrated in a particular region, then more molecules are more likely to spread to where they are less concentrated than to where they are more concentrated, even though each molecule is moving randomly in any direction. There is, therefore, a net movement of molecules down their concentration gradient: overall more molecules move in a particular direction than in any other direction.*

Facilitated diffusion

To enter or leave a cell, most hydrophilic molecules (and ions) diffuse through pores formed by different carrier proteins which cross from one side of the plasma membrane to the other. The process is called **facilitated diffusion**.

The pores of the different carrier proteins are filled with water, making a hydrophilic channel through the hydrophobic region of the phospholipid bilayer. So hydrophilic molecules (and ions) can pass through the channels and therefore through membranes more easily (the word 'facilitated' means 'made easy').

Pores are specific to the substances that pass through them. The rate at which a substance diffuses through the pores of a carrier protein depends on:

• the steepness of its concentration gradient across the membrane – the bigger the gradient, the greater is the rate of diffusion

• the type of carrier protein forming the pore – each type is the right size and structure to allow the passage of a particular substance

• the number of pores in the membrane – the more pores there are, the greater is the rate of diffusion

• whether the pores are open or not

Some pores are open all the time. Others are closed, but they open in the presence of a particular molecule (or ion). Such pores are said to be **gated**. The operation of nerves and muscles depends on gated channels for the movement of sodium ions (Na^+), potassium ions (K^+), and calcium ions (Ca^{2+}) into and out of nerve cells and muscle cells.

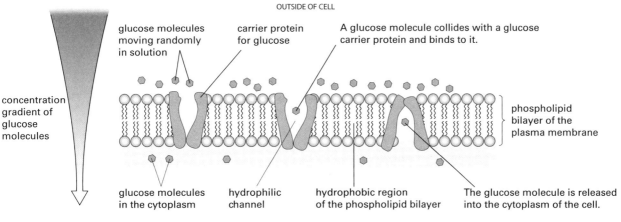

OUTSIDE OF CELL

glucose molecules moving randomly in solution

carrier protein for glucose

A glucose molecule collides with a glucose carrier protein and binds to it.

concentration gradient of glucose molecules

phospholipid bilayer of the plasma membrane

glucose molecules in the cytoplasm

hydrophilic channel

hydrophobic region of the phospholipid bilayer

The glucose molecule is released into the cytoplasm of the cell.

INSIDE OF CELL

Facilitated diffusion through the plasma membrane. Notice that the binding site for glucose on the carrier protein faces outwards in one state and into the cell in the other state. The attachment of the glucose molecule is responsible for the change in shape and results in the release of glucose into the cytoplasm of the cell.

As a substance passes through the membrane its carrier protein undergoes a change in tertiary or quaternary structure.

Osmosis

Osmosis is the net movement of water molecules through a partially permeable membrane from a region where they are in a higher concentration to a region where they are in a lower concentration. The term refers to the diffusion of water molecules and is only used in this context.

solution A
(dilute solution)

solution B
(concentrated solution)

HIGH CONCENTRATION OF WATER

net movement of water molecules

LOW CONCENTRATION OF WATER

partially permeable membrane

molecules of substance

concentration gradient of water

pore in membrane

water molecules

More water molecules on this side of membrane, so more water molecules pass from left to right.

Fewer water molecules on this side of membrane, so fewer water molecules pass from right to left.

Osmosis

Water potential

Water molecules in motion striking a membrane exert pressure called the **water potential**. The higher the concentration of water molecules, the greater is the kinetic energy of the system and the greater is the water potential. Water potential is measured in kilopascals (kPa).

In the diagram, solution A has a higher (less negative) water potential than solution B. There is a water potential gradient between the two solutions across the partially permeable membrane.

Stating the definition of osmosis in terms of water potential:

- Osmosis is the movement of water down a water potential gradient across a partially permeable membrane from a solution of a higher (less negative) water potential to a solution of a lower (more negative) water potential.

How science works (B)

Thinking about osmosis another way

Water potential is a measure of the free kinetic energy of the system.

- The higher the concentration of water molecules, the *greater* is the free kinetic energy of the system.

  Ⓡ As a result, a system in which the water molecules have *high* kinetic energy (there are *few* solute molecules in the system to obstruct them) will tend to lose more water than a system in which the water molecules have *low* kinetic energy (there are *more* solute molecules in the system).

- The water potential of pure water at atmospheric pressure is zero (0). The addition of a solute such as glucose lowers the water potential because there is a lower concentration of water molecules per unit volume of the solution.

  Ⓡ As a result the water potential of the solution has a negative value. The more solute is dissolved, the greater is the negative value. Also, more water molecules are attracted to solute molecules.

  Ⓡ As a result the water molecules in the system move less freely.

  Ⓡ As a result the kinetic energy of the system is lowered.

  Ⓡ As a result the water potential of the system is lowered.

  Ⓡ As a result the system will tend to lose less water than a system in which the water molecules have *high* kinetic energy.

Active transport

Sometimes molecules or ions move across membranes from where they are in lower concentration to where they are in higher concentration. In other words they move in the reverse direction to diffusion. The process is called **active transport** and allows cells to build up stores of a substance that would otherwise be spread out by diffusion. The storage of glucose by liver cells is an example.

- The process is **active** in the sense that more energy is required to move the molecules or ions against their concentration gradient than down it. This is the energy released by the hydrolysis of ATP which is produced during cellular respiration.

- Diffusion, facilitated diffusion, and osmosis are **passive** processes in the sense that energy provided by the hydrolysis of ATP is not required – the kinetic energy provided as the result of the kinetic motion of their molecules is sufficient to move molecules or ions down their concentration gradient.

Although active transport requires ATP and facilitated diffusion does not, the movement of molecules and ions by both processes is achieved by carrier proteins. Each type of carrier protein is specific for a particular molecule or ion.

The **sodium–potassium pump** is an example of a carrier protein which actively transports sodium (Na$^+$) ions and potassium (K$^+$) ions across the plasma membrane of cells.

Checklist for the sodium–potassium pump

1 • The concentration of sodium ions (Na$^+$) is higher outside the cell than inside.
- The concentration of potassium ions (K$^+$) is higher inside the cell than outside.
- Three Na$^+$ and one molecule of ATP bind to the pump protein.

2 • The ATP is hydrolysed and ADP is released. The phosphate group remains bound to the pump protein.
- As a result the shape of the pump protein changes.
- As a result the three Na$^+$ pass from the cell *against* the concentration gradient of Na$^+$ and are released.
- Two K$^+$ bind to the pump protein.

3 • The phosphate group bound to the pump protein is released.
- As a result the structure of the pump protein changes back to its original shape.
- As a result the two K$^+$ pass into the cell *against* the concentration gradient for K$^+$ and are released.

Notice in the diagram:
- The pump protein extends through the phospholipid bilayer.
- As a result the hydrophilic Na$^+$ and K$^+$ do not come into contact with the hydrophobic region of the plasma membrane.
- As a result Na$^+$ and K$^+$ pass through the membrane in opposite directions. For every three Na$^+$ removed from the cell, two K$^+$ are taken in.
- As a result the inner surface of the plasma membrane becomes negatively charged and a potential difference builds up across the membrane.

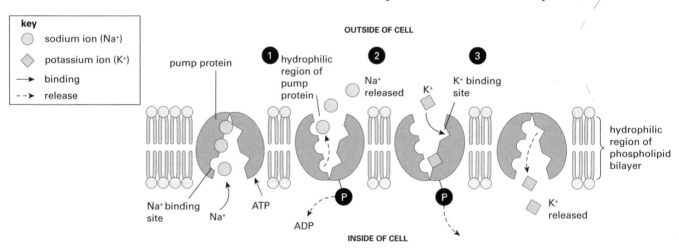

The sodium–potassium pump. Carrier proteins which transport substances in *opposite* directions are called **antiports**.

Questions

1 Explain the differences between the processes of diffusion, facilitated diffusion, and active transport.

2 Why might osmosis be described as a special case of diffusion?

3 Briefly describe osmosis in terms of a water potential gradient across a partially permeable membrane.

1.12 Absorption

OBJECTIVES

By the end of the section you should

○ *be able to identify the features that increase the area of the inner surface of the small intestine*

○ *understand by which processes the products of carbohydrate digestion are absorbed by the small intestine*

Before you start, it will help to read sections **1.03** (digestion), **1.10** (plasma membrane), **1.11** (diffusion and active transport), and **2.14** (surface area).

Surface area

The inner surface of the wall of the small intestine has folds, villi, and other features which greatly increase the surface area available to absorb the products of digestion. The diagram shows how these different features affect the orders of increase in surface area, compared with the internal surface area of a cylinder.

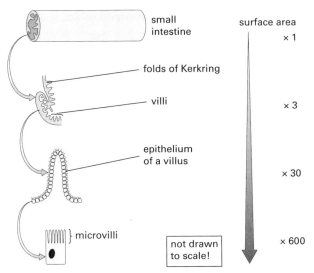

Notice that the surface of the cells of the epithelium lining the villi is thrown into tiny folds, visible only in the electron microscope. The folds are called **microvilli** and form what is often called the **brush border** because they look a little like the bristles of a brush.

Absorption

Absorption of the products of carbohydrate digestion begins in the duodenum, but most occurs across the wall of the ileum. It starts at the brush border of microvilli at the surface of each villus.

Molecules of sugar pass

- through the plasma membrane of each epithelial cell
- across each cell
- through the plasma membrane on the opposite side of each cell
- through the wall of a capillary blood vessel or the wall of a lacteal vessel

These vessels are parts of a network of vessels within each villus. The capillaries run into the hepatic portal vein; the lacteal vessels run into the lymphatic system. Passage of the molecules across the plasma membrane of the cells is by diffusion, facilitated diffusion, and active transport.

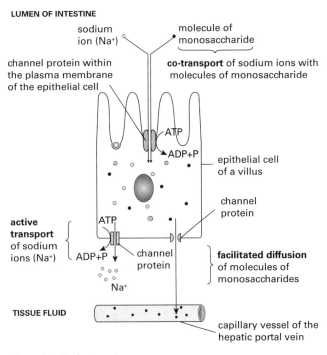

Absorption in the intestine

Notice the following.

- **Glucose** and other sugars are some of the products of digestion which pass into the hepatic portal vein to be transported in the bloodstream to the liver.
- **Carrier proteins** in the plasma membrane couple the transport of monosaccharides with sodium ions (Na^+) from the lumen of the intestine into the epithelial cells of the villi. The process is called **co-transport** because the movement of monosaccharides and sodium occurs together. The process is a form of active transport requiring ATP as a source of energy.
- **Monosaccharide** molecules transfer from the epithelial cells into capillary vessels of the hepatic portal vein by facilitated diffusion.
- **Sodium ions** (Na^+) are pumped from the base of epithelial cells into the surrounding tissue fluid by active transport. ATP is required as a source of energy.

Questions

1 Summarize the features of the small intestine which increase its internal surface area compared with the internal surface area of a cylinder.

2 Briefly explain how sugar molecules are absorbed by a cell lining the wall of the ileum (small intestine).

1.13 Cholera

OBJECTIVES

By the end of the section you should

○ know that cholera bacteria produce toxins which result in diarrhoea in the host

○ know the structure of the cholera bacterium as an example of a prokaryotic organism

○ understand the use of oral rehydration solutions in the treatment of diarrhoeal diseases

○ be able to discuss issues around developments in the improvement of oral rehydration solutions

Before you start, it will help to read section **1.11** (osmosis and active transport–Fick's law).

Cholera

Cholera is caused by *Vibrio cholerae*. The bacterium is carried in water and transferred to food by flies. It produces a toxin in the intestines, resulting in vomiting and the passing of large volumes of liquid faeces (diarrhoea). Without proper treatment the affected person can die within 24 hours.

Structure of the cholera bacterium

The cholera bacterium is an example of a **prokaryotic cell**. All bacterial cells are prokaryotic. They are microorganisms – so called because they can just be seen with the optical microscope. The transmission electron microscope shows their detailed structure.

slime capsule (not present in all bacteria)

glycogen granule

plasma membrane

Cell wall protects the bacterium, has a shape characteristic of the bacterium. Made of lipid, protein and a carbohydrate other than cellulose.

cytoplasm

Flagellum (not present in all bacteria). There may be more than one flagellum. They are used to propel the bacterium through liquid.

No distinct nucleus. Strands of DNA are located in the cytoplasm. In some bacteria DNA is circular. The term plasmid refers to circular DNA.

Ribosomes – sites of protein synthesis. Bacterial ribosomes are smaller than those found in eukaryotic cells.

The cholera bacterium *Vibrio cholerae*

- Notice that the cell lacks a distinct nucleus (the term prokaryotic literally means 'before the nucleus').
- Notice also the absence of many of the other structures found in eurkaryotic cells.

How the bacterium causes diarrhoea

Cholera bacteria bind tightly to the epithelial cells (host cells) lining the intestine. The following sequence then takes place.

- Cholera toxin stimulates the epithelial cells to pump chloride ions (Cl^-) into the lumen (space) of the intestine.
- This lowers the water potential of the intestine's contents. Water passes down the water potential gradient from the epithelial cells into the intestine.
- Water and ions lost from the epithelial cells are replaced by water from the blood. The cells become pumps for water and ions, causing the severe diarrhoea.
- The loss of water from the body quickly leads to dehydration. The loss of ions causes severe cramps and may lead to heart failure.

Oral rehydration therapy

It is essential to replace promptly the water and ions lost because of the victim's severe diarrhoea. The treatment is called **oral rehydration therapy (ORT)**. At its simplest the treatment consists of the victim drinking a mixture of salts and sugars dissolved in water.

ORT is cheap and saves millions of lives each year from cholera and other diseases which cause diarrhoea – particularly children where dehydration caused by diarrhoea is a major cause of death.

Simply drinking water is ineffective. The salts in ORT solution replace the ions, especially sodium (Na^+) and potassium (K^+), lost in the victim's liquid faeces. The sugars are essential for absorption of the ions and water. The diagram illustrates the mechanism.

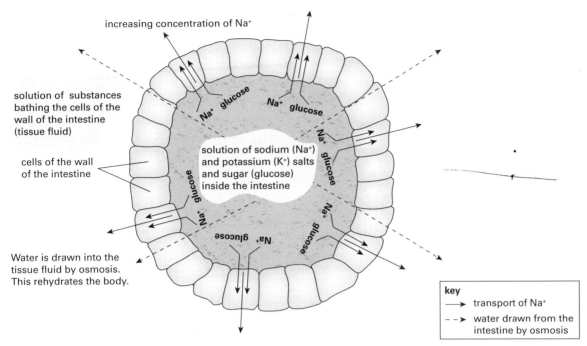

increasing concentration of Na⁺

solution of substances bathing the cells of the wall of the intestine (tissue fluid)

cells of the wall of the intestine

solution of sodium (Na⁺) and potassium (K⁺) salts and sugar (glucose) inside the intestine

Water is drawn into the tissue fluid by osmosis. This rehydrates the body.

key
→ transport of Na⁺
- - → water drawn from the intestine by osmosis

How oral rehydration therapy works. The intestine is shown here in cross-section. As sodium (Na⁺) is transported through the cells of the wall of the intestine, water is drawn from the intestine by osmosis to rehydrate the body.

- Active transport by one type of carrier protein moves sodium ions (Na⁺) and glucose molecules from the lumen of the intestine into the epithelial cells lining the intestine. The carrier protein is an example of a **synport**.
- Here another carrier protein actively transports the Na⁺ out of the epithelial cells into the tissue fluid surrounding the cells.
- The increasing concentration of Na⁺ in the tissue fluid lowers its water potential.
  - As a result water passes down the water potential gradient from the lumen of the intestine into the epithelial cells and from the epithelial cells to the tissue fluid by osmosis.

The treatment prevents further life threatening dehydration until the victim's diarrhoea stops and recovery begins.

Improving oral rehydration therapy

Unfortunately the original formulation of salts and sugars in ORT solution takes time to work. The life-threatening dehydration may stop but the diarrhoea continues. Victims think the treatment is failing, lose confidence, and look for alternatives. These may be more expensive and less suitable.

A new formulation of ORT solution is going some way to restoring confidence:

- Fewer salts and sugars in the ORT solution results in fewer failed treatments.
- Adding zinc for two or three weeks to the solution given to children reduces diarrhoea, and in the short term protects the child from it reoccurring.

However problems remain. Early trials did not clearly show that the new formulation was more effective than the original. Did the new formulation just make fewer people feel better or were any improvements real? Some doctors are not convinced and more trials are needed.

Fact file

- Carrier proteins which transport substances in *opposite* directions are called **antiports**.

- Carrier proteins which transport substances in *the same* direction are called **synports**.

Questions

1 Why does a person infected with cholera bacteria suffer from severe diarrhoea?

2 Explain why oral rehydration therapy is often a successful treatment for people suffering from diseases which cause diarrhoea.

3 List some of the differences in structure between a prokaryotic cell and a eukaryotic cell.

1.14 Lungs and breathing

OBJECTIVES

By the end of the section you should

○ know the important structures of the human gas exchange system

○ know the features of the alveolar epithelium as a surface where the exchange of gases occurs

○ understand how the exchange of gases takes place

○ understand the mechanism of breathing

○ know the relationship between tidal volume, ventilation rate, and pulmonary ventilation

Before you start, it will help to read sections **1.11** (diffusion) and **2.14** (diffusion across membranes).

The diagram helps you to locate and identify the important structures of the human gas exchange system.

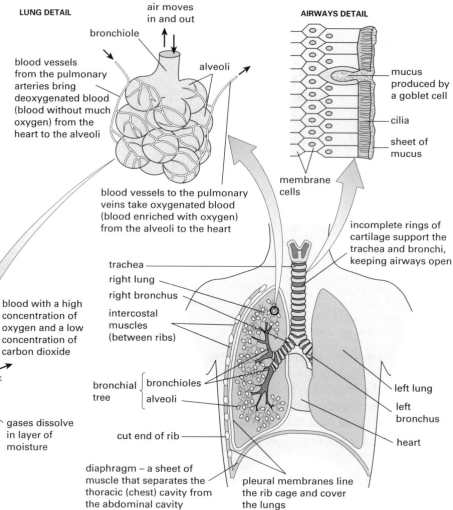

LUNG DETAIL

air moves in and out

bronchiole

blood vessels from the pulmonary arteries bring deoxygenated blood (blood without much oxygen) from the heart to the alveoli

alveoli

blood vessels to the pulmonary veins take oxygenated blood (blood enriched with oxygen) from the alveoli to the heart

AIRWAYS DETAIL

mucus produced by a goblet cell

cilia

sheet of mucus

membrane cells

incomplete rings of cartilage support the trachea and bronchi, keeping airways open

trachea
right lung
right bronchus
intercostal muscles (between ribs)

bronchial tree { bronchioles / alveoli

cut end of rib

diaphragm – a sheet of muscle that separates the thoracic (chest) cavity from the abdominal cavity

pleural membranes line the rib cage and cover the lungs

left lung
left bronchus
heart

ALVEOLUS DETAIL

blood with a low concentration of oxygen and a high concentration of carbon dioxide

blood with a high concentration of oxygen and a low concentration of carbon dioxide

red blood cells absorb oxygen

CO₂ diffuses out of blood   O₂ diffuses into blood

gases dissolve in layer of moisture

wall of capillary – only one cell thick

wall of alveolus – only one cell thick

Notice that

• the **trachea** (windpipe) branches into two bronchi

• each bronchus branches into many **bronchioles**

• each bronchiole ends in a cluster of **alveoli** (air sacs)

• the alveoli honeycomb lung tissue

Notice also

• A network of capillary vessels supply blood to and carry blood *from* the alveoli.

• The walls of the alveoli and capillary vessels are each one cell thick.

  ⓡ As a result a surface only two cells thick separates the air in the alveolus and the blood in the capillary blood vessel.

  ⓡ As a result the diffusion of gases (oxygen and carbon dioxide) across the surface is rapid.

The rate of diffusion of gases across the surface of the alveoli depends on concentration gradients. Inhalation (breathing in) draws air into the alveoli.

• The concentration of oxygen of inhaled air in the alveoli is greater than the concentration of oxygen in the blood supplied to the alveoli.

  ⓡ As a result oxygen diffuses down its concentration gradient from the air in the alveoli to the blood in the capillary vessels supplying the alveoli.

• The concentration of carbon dioxide in the blood supplied to the alveoli is greater than that in the inhaled air in the alveoli.

  ⓡ As a result carbon dioxide diffuses down its concentration gradient from the blood in the capillary vessels supplying the alveoli to the air in the alveoli.

Exhalation (breathing out) carries air out of the lungs. The table shows the percentage change in oxygen and carbon dioxide of inhaled and exhaled air.

Breathing in and breathing out

The cage around the **thoracic** (chest) **cavity** formed by the ribs and diaphragm is elastic. As it moves the pressure of air in the lungs changes. The change in air pressure causes **inhalation** (breathing in) and **exhalation** (breathing out). These repeated breathing movements ventilate the lungs.

Gas	% by volume in inhaled air	% by volume in exhaled air
oxygen	21	16
carbon dioxide	0.035	4

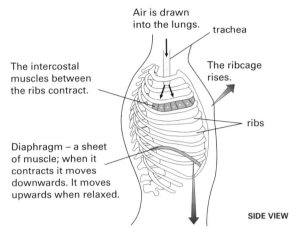

The diaphragm contracts and flattens.

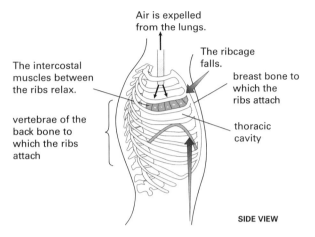

The diaphragm relaxes and curves upwards.

Inhalation

- The diaphragm contracts and becomes less dome-shaped.
- At the same time the intercostal muscles between the ribs contract and raise the rib cage.
- The thoracic cavity enlarges. The resulting reduction in air pressure is transmitted via the **pleural cavity** to the lungs.
- The pressure of air in the alveoli is *less* than that of the atmosphere. Air, therefore, is drawn into the lungs through the trachea and bronchi.

Exhalation

- The diaphragm and intercostal muscles relax, lowering the ribs and raising the diaphragm.
- The volume of the thoracic cavity decreases and the lungs are compressed.
- The pressure of air in the alveoli is *greater* than that of the atmosphere.
- The air passes from the lungs through the bronchi and trachea to the atmosphere.

The pleural cavity is the space between the lungs and the rib cage. It is lined by **pleural membranes**. The membranes are lubricated, facilitating (making easy) movements of the lungs. Gas pressure within the pleural cavity is less than that of the atmosphere.

Changes in the volume of inhaled and exhaled air

The volume of air exchanged between the lungs and the atmosphere depends on the body's activity and the extent and rate of ventilation (measured as the breathing rate) of the lungs. The volume of air breathed in and out is measured using a **spirometer**.

- The air capacity of the human lungs is about 5.5 dm³, of which 1.5 dm³ is the **residual volume**. The term refers to the air *not removed* from the lungs even when breathing is forced.
- At rest, normal breathing results in a **tidal volume** of around 0.5 dm³. So a person with a resting breathing rate of 16 inhalations/exhalations per minute exchanges air at a rate of 16 × 0.5 = 8 dm³ min⁻¹.
- Stress and strenuous physical activity increase the breathing rate and so increase the rate at which air is exchanged. The whole volume of the lungs less its residual volume comes into play. The volume is about 4.0 dm³ (5.5 dm³ − 1.5 dm³) and represents the **vital capacity** of the lungs. For example, a breathing rate of 40 inhalations/exhalations per minute exchanges air at a rate of 40 × 4.0 = 160 dm³ min⁻¹.

Changes in breathing rate help to keep the levels of oxygen and carbon dioxide in the blood constant.

Questions

1 Summarize the features of the alveolar epithelium as a gas exchange surface.

2 Explain how the diffusion of oxygen and carbon dioxide across the surface of the alveoli depends on their respective concentration gradients.

3 Summarize the changes in air pressure in the lungs during one cycle of inhalation and exhalation.

4 Explain the relationship between residual volume, tidal volume, and vital capacity of the lungs.

1.15　Lung disease

OBJECTIVES

By the end of the section you should

○ *understand the biology of pulmonary tuberculosis*

○ *know the effects of fibrosis, asthma, and emphysema on lung function*

○ *be able to interpret data that helped establish the link between smoking and lung cancer*

Before you start, it will help to read sections **1.02** (smoking and cancer) and **1.14** (lungs and breathing).

Tuberculosis

Tuberculosis (TB) is caused by *Mycobacterium tuberculosis*. The bacterium is air-borne. It passes from person to person in droplets of moisture when infected people talk, laugh, cough, or sneeze. Overcrowded living conditions provide an ideal environment for rapid spread of the disease.

Once breathed in, TB bacteria lodge in the lungs. From here the bacteria may pass into the blood, which carries them to other tissues of the body. For example, they may infect lymphatic tissue. Symptoms include swelling of the lymph glands and the development of abscesses.

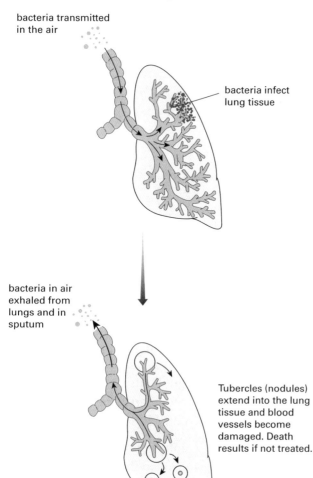

bacteria transmitted in the air

bacteria infect lung tissue

bacteria in air exhaled from lungs and in sputum

Tubercles (nodules) extend into the lung tissue and blood vessels become damaged. Death results if not treated.

Lungs infected with tuberculosis

Pulmonary TB

This is the most common form of the disease. Once in the lungs, the bacteria multiply. There are two phases:

- **TB infection** – the affected person may develop a dry cough for 3–4 months before the cough clears up
- **TB disease** – the affected person coughs violently and frequently, bringing up phlegm which may be tinged with blood. Onset of the disease may occur months or years after infection.

Only about 10% of people with TB infection go on to develop TB disease. In most infected people, the body's immune system keeps the TB bacteria in check. The bacteria become inactive and lie dormant in the body's tissues – in many cases, for many years. People with TB infection show no symptoms of the disease and cannot infect other people.

However, some people are vulnerable to TB infection developing into TB disease. These are people with

- a weakened immune system (people infected with HIV are particularly at risk)
- some other types of lung disease

Treatment involves the victim taking a combination of antibiotics. The drugs only slowly clear the body of the bacteria, so treatment must continue for many months.

Effects of disease on lung function

Lung disease may make breathing more difficult, causing breathlessness. **Fibrosis** and **asthma** are examples.

Fibrosis

Fibrosis is a chronic (long-term) disease of the lungs. It causes inflammation and scarring of the many thousands of alveoli throughout lung tissue.

As the disease develops, the alveoli (and the capillary vessels which supply blood to them) are twisted out of shape. Eventually the lung tissue thickens and becomes stiff. The loss of flexibility causes the breathlessness associated with fibrosis.

Causes of fibrosis are often difficult to identify. Known causes may be

- work-related – where people's jobs place them in dusty environments. Mining work which produces metal dust or stone dust is an example. **Asbestosis** is caused when needle-like particles of asbestos are inhaled. The particles can cause fibrosis and may eventually lead to lung cancer
- ionizing radiation – used to treat cancers affecting the chest
- chronic conditions – such as rheumatoid arthritis

Treatment that may be effective includes

- removing the victim from the environment causing the condition
- dealing with the underlying disease causing the condition

Otherwise slow deterioration as a result of the progressive scarring of the lungs is the usual outcome.

Asthma

Asthma is a common condition. It is caused by obstruction to the flow of air through the airways. Attacks of wheezing, difficulty with breathing, and a feeling of tightness in the chest are symptoms often experienced by asthma sufferers.

Obstruction to the flow of air is due to the narrowing of the airways. Narrowing is the result of inflammation of the walls of the airways. In severe cases plugs of mucus may block them. Airflow is obstructed even more.

Smoking and lung disease

Research begun in the 1930s gathered data which by the 1970s established the link between smoking, lung cancer, and other diseases.

> You do not need to learn these graphs, but may need to interpret them (or similar) in the exam.

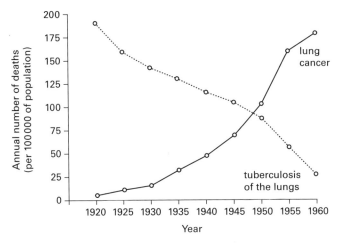

Deaths from lung disease in England and Wales from 1920 to 1960. Deaths from lung cancer increased sharply when deaths from tuberculosis fell.

- Doctors quickly realized the possible significance of the data. Many gave up smoking. Deaths from lung cancer among doctors went down compared with the population as a whole, who were less well informed.
- Further studies established the correlation between the risk of dying from lung cancer and the number of cigarettes smoked – the more cigarettes smoked, the greater the risk.

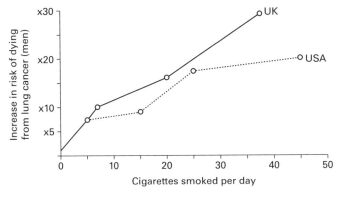

Death rates from lung cancer in men who smoke

Emphysema

Smoking is also the cause of **emphysema**. Its symptoms include breathlessness and exhaustion.

- The substances in tobacco smoke stimulate cells (called mast cells) in the lungs to produce protein-digesting enzymes.
- The enzymes catalyse reactions which destroy the alveoli, creating enlarged cavities.
  - Ⓡ As a result the surface area of lung tissue available for the absorption of oxygen therefore decreases.
  - Ⓡ As a result oxygenation of the blood is reduced. Even a small increase in physical effort makes the person breathless and exhausted.

Questions

1 How does the bacterium which cause tuberculosis pass from person to person?
2 What is the difference between fibrosis and asthma?
3 Why do people suffering from emphysema quickly become breathless and exhausted?

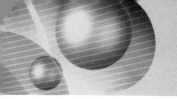

OBJECTIVES

By the end of the section you should

○ *know the structure and function of the heart and its associated blood vessels*

○ *understand the cardiac cycle*

○ *understand how the contraction of heart muscle is coordinated*

○ *know the relationship between cardiac output, heart rate, and stroke volume*

Heart structure and function

Heartbeat

Heartbeats are the result of the contraction and relaxation of the **cardiac** muscle of the heart. This action pumps blood through the system of blood vessels which make up the circulatory system.

Each beat is a two-tone sound made by the opening and closing of the valves which direct the flow of blood through the heart. A natural pacemaker located in the wall of the heart controls the heartbeat.

Heart structure

The heart lies in the chest cavity, protected by the rib cage. Inside it has four chambers, separated by a septum into the right-hand side and left-hand side. Outside, vessels supply blood to its surface. The diagrams show the arrangement.

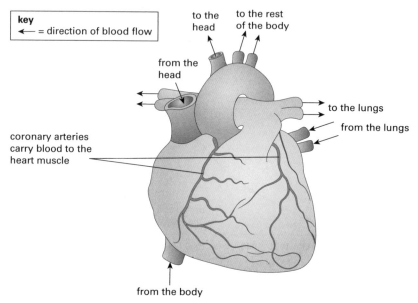

Blood supply to and from the heart (viewed from the front)

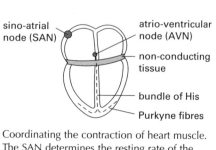

Coordinating the contraction of heart muscle. The SAN determines the resting rate of the heartbeat and is called the **pacemaker**. Nerve impulses from the SAN to the AVN are prevented from reaching the ventricles by the band of non-impulse-conducting tissue in the wall of the heart.

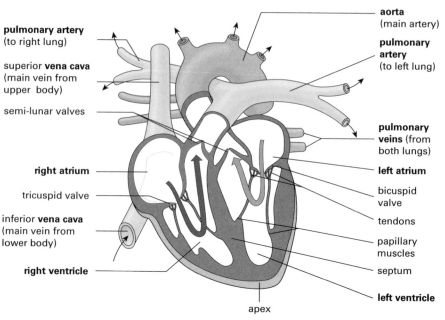

A vertical section through the heart (viewed from the front)

The cardiac cycle

The term **cardiac cycle** refers to the sequence of events which propel blood through the heart and its associated blood vessels. Use the diagram to follow the sequence.

Step 1 – Atrial diastole

- The atria are relaxed. The valves separating the atria from the ventricles are closed.
- The right atrium fills with deoxygenated blood from the venae cavae. The left atrium fills with oxygenated blood from the pulmonary veins.
- As the atria fill, increasing pressure is put on the valves. They start to open.

1

Deoxygenated blood draining from the tissues enters the right atrium.

valve closed

valve closed

Oxygenated blood draining from the lungs enters the left atrium.

To begin with the valve is closed.

left ventricle

right ventricle

Step 2 – Atrial systole

- Nerve impulses generated in the **sino-atrial node (SAN)** spread out through the muscles of the atria.
- The atria contract. Their volume decreases so the pressure of blood inside increases.
- Blood is forced through the valves into the ventricles.
- The impulses from the SAN stimulate the atrio-ventricular node (AVN) in the septum separating the atria.
- Impulses from the AVN pass along the **Bundle of His** which is made up of strands of conductive tissue called **Purkyne fibres** (also called Purkinje fibres).

2

The vein contracts where it joins the atrium, preventing the backflow of blood as the pressure within the atrium increases.

valve closed

valve closed

The vein contracts where it joins the atrium, preventing the backflow of blood as the pressure within the atrium increases.

valve opens

Blood enters the ventricles.

valve opens

Step 3 – Ventricular systole

- The wave of impulses from the bundle of His stimulates the muscle of the walls of the ventricles at their apex.
- The ventricles contract from the apex upwards. Their volume decreases so the pressure of the blood inside increases.
- This forces shut the valves separating the atria from the ventricles (preventing backflow into the atria), and opens the valves guarding the openings of the arteries.
- Blood is forced through the pulmonary artery and the aorta.
- The elasticity of the artery walls allows for the increase in the volume of blood. Back flow into the ventricles is prevented by the semi-lunar valves.

3

Blood is forced into the artery and passes to the lungs.

valve opens

valve opens

Blood is forced into the main artery through which it passes to the body's tissues.

valve closed

valve closed

apex of ventricles

Step 4 – Ventricular diastole

- Relaxation of the ventricles marks the end of the cardiac cycle.

Step	Time in seconds
atrial systole	0.1
ventricular systole	0.3
atrial and ventricular diastole	0.4
Total time	**0.8**

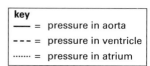

key
— = pressure in aorta
- - - = pressure in ventricle
······ = pressure in atrium

Fact file

The heart can contract and relax rhythmically for a considerable time without the stimulus of nerve impulses or hormones. We say that the heart beat is **myogenic**. The term means that contraction originates in the heart itself.

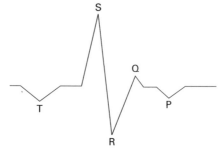
An ECG of a heartbeat

Questions

1 Describe the events of the cardiac cycle.

2 Name the waves which form the trace of an ECG.

3 Explain the relationship between cardiac output, heart rate, and stroke volume.

Timings and pressure changes

The table shows the average timings during one cardiac cycle of a resting person. These timings and the corresponding changes in pressure in the atria, ventricles, and aorta are summarized in the diagram.

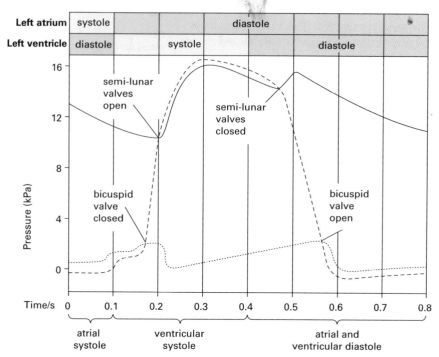

Pressure changes during the cardiac cycle. The maximal pressure in the left ventricle is greater than in the right ventricle because the wall of the left ventricle is thicker so it contracts more powerfully. The opening and closing of the different valves depends on the relative pressure on either side of each one.

Measuring heartbeat

The electrical activity of the heart's nerves and muscles can be detected by electrodes placed on the body's surface. The output is a series of waves in the form of a trace called an **ECG (electrocardiogram)**.

• The **P wave** records current flow through the atria from the SAN → AVN.
• The **QRS waves** record the spread of electrical activity through the ventricles.
• The **T wave** records the current generated following contraction of the ventricles.

An ECG is a picture of the heart's electrical activity and helps doctors diagnose its health.

The heart at work

The healthy heart at rests beats on average between 60 and 80 beats per minute: this is the **heart rate**.

The volume of blood pumped from the heart each minute (**cardiac output**) depends on the heart rate and volume of blood pumped out with each beat (**stroke volume**).

Heart rate, stroke volume, and cardiac output measure the heart's effectiveness and fitness:

cardiac output = heart rate × stroke volume

A fit heart, at rest, has 25% more output than an unfit heart. During vigorous exercise output is 50% more and this meets the increased demand for oxygen from the muscles more efficiently. Stroke volume is also greater and a fit heart beats more slowly.

1.17 Heart disease

OBJECTIVES

By the end of the section you should

○ *know what atheroma is*

○ *understand the link between atheroma, aneurysm, and thrombosis*

○ *understand the cause of myocardial infarction*

Before you start, it will help to read sections **1.02** (heart disease) and **1.16** (heart structure).

Coronary arteries

The **coronary arteries** run over and deep into the walls of the heart. They transport blood with supplies of dissolved oxygen and nutrients needed by the heart muscles.

It may seem odd that the heart needs its own blood supply, when its chambers are filled with blood. But its walls are so thick that oxygen and nutrients in the blood inside the heart would not be able to diffuse into all of the heart muscle.

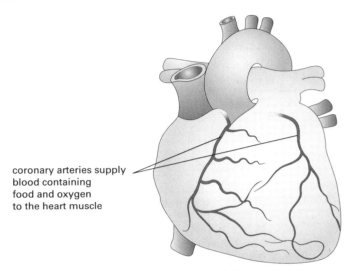

coronary arteries supply blood containing food and oxygen to the heart muscle

The coronary arteries pass over and penetrate the wall of the heart.

The smooth inner wall of healthy blood vessels allows blood to flow easily through them. Anticoagulants such as **heparin** (produced by the liver) and **prostacyclin** (produced by the lining of blood vessels) prevent blood from clotting inside vessels.

Atheroma and sclerosis of the heart

Normally streaks of fat occur in the inner layer of arteries. However, in time, fatty material (**atheroma**) may accumulate in localized deposits called **plaques**. Large amounts of **cholesterol** are found in atheroma.

As atheroma builds up it may 'harden' because of the deposition of fibrous material and/or calcium salts (**calcification**). The hardening process is called 'sclerosis' and the result is **atherosclerosis** of the arteries.

Angina

In time, plaques may narrow the arteries so much that insufficient blood reaches the tissue beyond the constriction. If the coronary arteries are narrowed, the first signs of trouble may be breathlessness and a cramp-like pain in the chest. This pain is called **angina**. It can be brought on by quick walking, anger, excitement, or anything else that makes the heart work harder than usual.

Angina is the heart's response to being starved of the oxygen that blood carries. People live with some types of angina for years, but other types get worse and may later result in a heart attack.

Fact file

Different types of **nitrate drug** have been used for many years to treat the symptoms of angina. **Glycerol trinitrate** is one of the most effective. It dilates (makes wider) the coronary arteries, improving the blood supply to the heart muscle and relieving chest pain.

How science works (K)

Testing new drugs

All claims made for the medical benefits of a new drug have to be supported by scientific evidence. Drug manufacturers, therefore, have to carry out a rigorous testing programme before bringing a new drug to market.

Testing begins in the laboratory on preparations of cells, tissues and even whole organs. This is called *in-vitro* (literally 'in glass') testing. If the results are promising, then the next step is to test the effect of the substance in animals. This is called *in-vivo* (literally 'in life') testing.

Clinical trials of the proposed drug on humans can begin only when the results of animal studies have been validated by members of the scientific community. Once these are complete, the results are sent to an independent panel of experts to evaluate the drug. If the members of the panel conclude that the drug provides real benefit to patients, then the manufacturers can apply for a product licence and begin to market the drug.

Testing new drugs on animals is controversial. Some people think that developments in tissue culture and computer modelling mean that it is no longer necessary to undertake animal studies as part of the programme of validating new drugs.

Heart attack

When the reduction in blood supply beyond an obstruction in the coronary arteries is so severe as to interrupt the blood supply, then the result is a **heart attack**.

- The victim may feel sick and faint, and pain usually grips the chest, spreading to the arms, neck, and jaw.
- Other signs of heart attack are sweating, breathlessness, and a pale skin because blood is not reaching the body's surface.

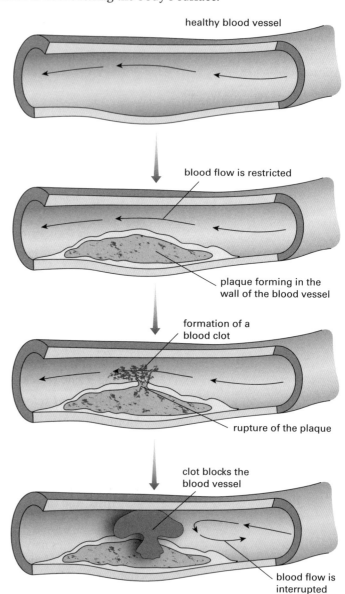

healthy blood vessel

blood flow is restricted

plaque forming in the wall of the blood vessel

formation of a blood clot

rupture of the plaque

clot blocks the blood vessel

blood flow is interrupted

key
← = direction of blood flow

Heart attack – a plaque in the wall of a coronary artery ruptures and a clot forms.

The events cause blockage in the blood vessels so that oxygen and nutrients cannot reach the heart muscle which the affected part of the coronary artery normally supplies. The tissue is damaged and may die.

- The clot is called a **thrombus** and the blockage a **thrombosis** – hence 'coronary thrombosis'. The term is often used to refer to a heart attack.
- **Myocardial infarction** is another term – 'myocardial' refers to the heart muscle, 'infarction' to the death of the muscle cells.

Cardiac arrest

A severe heart attack may start a rhythm disturbance called **ventricular fibrillation**, resulting in **cardiac arrest**. The electrical activity of the ventricles is so disturbed that the heart cannot pump any blood. The person becomes unconscious, and the pulse and breathing stop. It is essential to get the heart pumping again within a few minutes, otherwise the person will die.

Questions

1. The heart is filled with blood. Why does it need its own blood supply?
2. Explain the relationship between atheroma, atherosclerosis, and a heart attack.
3. Name two naturally occurring anticoagulants.

1.18 Principles of immunology

OBJECTIVES

By the end of the section you should

○ *know the meaning of different terms in immunology*

○ *understand the roles of B cells, T cells, and phagocytes in the immune response*

○ *be able to explain the primary and secondary immune responses*

○ *understand the problems of antigenic variability in the influenza virus*

Before you start, it will help to read section **1.01** (pathogens).

The immune response

When any type of 'foreign' material infects the blood or tissues, different types of white blood cell act quickly to destroy it.

- Such 'foreign' material includes viruses, bacteria, or any other cells or substances which the body does not recognize as its own.
- The white blood cells that destroy them include lymphocytes and phagocytes, and form part of the body's **immune system**.
- Their actions are the body's **immune response**.

Key words	
Pathogen	Any living thing that enters the body, causing disease. Different types of bacteria and viruses are common pathogens.
Immune response	All of the reactions of the body that make an invading pathogen harmless.
Antigen	Any substance that enters the body and stimulates the development of an immune response because the body does not recognize the substance as its own. Toxins released by parasites, proteins in the plasma membrane of bacterial cells, and proteins forming the 'coat' surrounding viruses act as antigens.
Antibody	Proteins called immunoglobulins produced by the B cells of the immune system as part of the response to the presence of antigen.
Lymphocytes	Types of white blood cell. These include B cells and T cells.
B cells	These produce antibodies (**humoral immunity**) in the presence of antigens.
T cells	These *do not* produce antibodies but have a variety of effects (**cell-mediated immunity**) in the presence of antigens.
Memory cells	Lymphocytes that survive for a long period (years or even a lifetime) following an immune response. If the body is infected again by the pathogen which provoked the initial immune response, then the memory cells rapidly divide, producing new lymphocytes which destroy the pathogen before the symptoms of disease appear.
Phagocytes	Types of white blood cell which engulf bacteria, viruses, and other antigenic components, destroying them.

The response of B cells and phagocytes

B cells divide and produce clones of cells in response to the detection of antigens. Most of the cells of these clones are **plasma** cells. They produce antibodies which combine with the antigens. The combinations are called **immune complexes**.

If immune complexes form between antibodies and the antigenic proteins in the plasma membrane of bacterial cells, the bacteria clump together (**agglutination**). Agglutination facilitates (makes easy) destruction of the bacteria by phagocytes (**phagocytosis**).

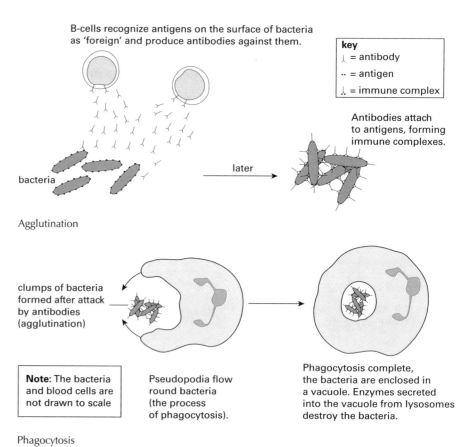

B-cells recognize antigens on the surface of bacteria as 'foreign' and produce antibodies against them.

key
⅄ = antibody
·· = antigen
⅄ = immune complex

bacteria

later

Antibodies attach to antigens, forming immune complexes.

Agglutination

clumps of bacteria formed after attack by antibodies (agglutination)

Note: The bacteria and blood cells are not drawn to scale

Pseudopodia flow round bacteria (the process of phagocytosis).

Phagocytosis complete, the bacteria are enclosed in a vacuole. Enzymes secreted into the vacuole from lysosomes destroy the bacteria.

Phagocytosis

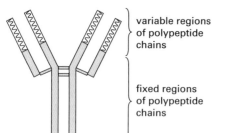

variable regions of polypeptide chains

fixed regions of polypeptide chains

The basic structure of an antibody

Why are antibodies specific?

A molecule of antibody is Y-shaped and made up of four polypeptide chains. The sequence of amino acid units of the 'stem' of the Y is **constant** but the sequence of amino acid units of the parts that make up the 'arms' of the Y is very **variable**.

Antibodies are specific because

- millions of variations in the sequence of amino acid units of the 'arms' are possible, so millions of different shapes of antibody are possible
- when B cells recognize a particular antigen, they produce a particular antibody in response – the shape of that antibody matches the shape of the antigen. It is specific to that antigen

Antibody and antigen combine at the variable regions of the antibody (the 'arms' of the Y shape) and an immune complex forms.

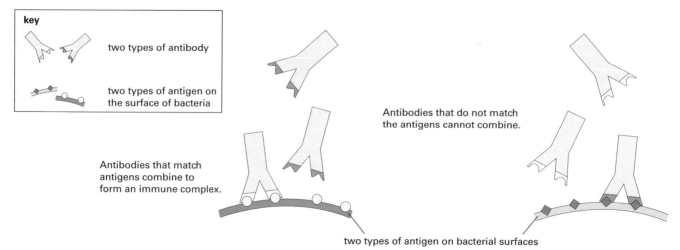

key

two types of antibody

two types of antigen on the surface of bacteria

Antibodies that do not match the antigens cannot combine.

Antibodies that match antigens combine to form an immune complex.

two types of antigen on bacterial surfaces

An immune complex forms when the shape of the antibody and antigen match.

The response of T cells

Different types of T cell have a number of roles in the immune response.
For example, **T-cytotoxic** (killer) cells attach to virus-infected cells, causing
them to burst (**lysis**). Antibodies prevent the virus particles released by lysis
from infecting other cells. Further infection is also prevented by the virus-
infected cells themselves before they burst. They release a protein called
interferon which stops the virus from replicating.

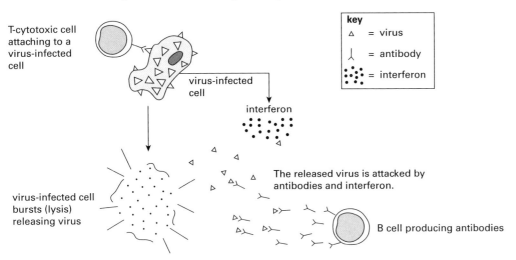

A T-cytotoxic cell attacking a virus-infected cell

Other types of T cell coordinate responses overall to the presence of antigens.
The diagram summarizes the interactions between B cells, T cells, and
phagocytes in the immune response.

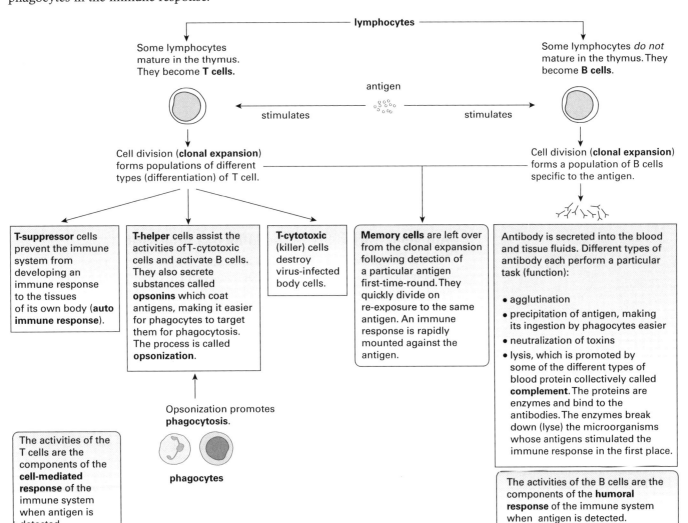

Immunological memory

On first encounter with an antigen, it takes the body a few days to produce antibodies (the **primary response**) against the infection. But on encountering the same antigens again, the response is much quicker (the **secondary response**). This is because of the presence of **memory cells**.

- B-memory cells rapidly produce plasma cells which then produce antibodies (see graph).
- T-memory cells produce plasma cells which then take part in cell-mediated immunity responses (details not needed).

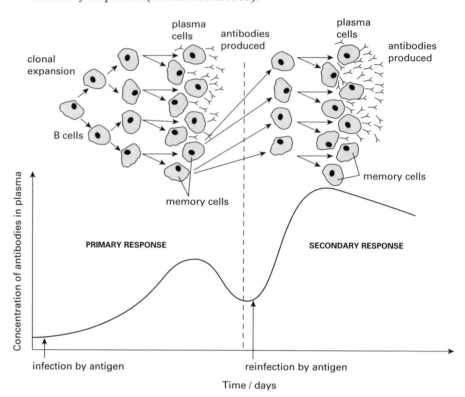

The primary and secondary responses of B cells

These enhanced responses are evidence for immunological memory, and memory cells are responsible for the effect.

Memory cells are specific for a particular antigen. This is why we do not catch mumps or chicken pox more than once in a lifetime: the rapid response as a result of immunological memory destroys the viruses which cause these diseases before they make us ill.

Antigenic variability in the influenza ('flu) virus

The surface proteins of 'flu viruses are antigens against which an infected person produces antibodies. But people may catch 'flu more than once during their lifetime. So why are the antibodies ineffective against 'flu virus when it next invades the body? After all, the production of memory cells means that we rarely catch diseases like chicken pox and measles more than once.

Unfortunately, frequent mutation means that 'flu virus antigens often change shape.

- Minor changes are called **antigenic drift**. They produce new **strains** of virus which are probably responsible for the frequent occurrence of 'flu **epidemics**.
- Major changes are called **antigenic shift** and result in new **types** of virus. They are less frequent and seem to be linked to the 10–20 year cycle of worldwide **pandemics**.

Antigenic drift and antigenic shift means that antibodies produced against a particular type of 'flu virus do not protect the person from infection by new variants of the virus. It also means that producing an effective vaccine is difficult.

Questions

1 What is an immune response?

2 Describe the different responses of B cells and T cells in the presence of an antigen.

3 Explain the difference between antigenic drift and antigenic shift in the 'flu virus.

1.19 Vaccines and monoclonal antibodies

OBJECTIVES

By the end of the section you should

○ *understand how vaccines protect individuals and populations against disease*

○ *know that monoclonal antibodies make it possible to target particular substances*

Before you start, it will help to read section **1.18** (immune response).

Vaccines

A **vaccine** is a preparation of dead or **attenuated** (weakened) pathogens or harmless components of pathogens which stimulate an immune response in a person receiving the vaccine. It can be given orally (by mouth) or by injection.

Following vaccination, the person is protected from the effects of the active form of the pathogen should it infect the body. We say that the person is **immune** to the pathogen. The immunity is **active** because the person's immune system has been stimulated to produce memory cells. These are the basis of the person's immunity. Active immunity is long-lasting.

Passive immunity comes from the injection of antibodies produced by another animal (e.g. horse). Protection against the effects of a particular pathogen is immediate. However, protection is short term.

The table summarizes the different types of vaccines.

Vaccine made from ...	Description	Examples
dead pathogens	The pathogens are killed by heat or the addition of chemicals such as formaldehyde. They do not cause disease, but the structures of the pathogen's surface molecules are preserved. The molecules can therefore act as antigens and stimulate antibody production in the person receiving the vaccine.	whooping cough vaccine Salk vaccine against poliomyelitis
weakened live form of the pathogen	Vaccines made in this way are called **attenuated vaccines**. The attenuated (weakened) pathogen infects the person receiving the vaccine, stimulating the production of antibodies. It does not cause disease.	BCG vaccine against tuberculosis Sabin vaccine taken orally against poliomyelitis
substances made from parts of the pathogen or its toxins	Inactivation makes the toxic substances (called **toxoids**) harmless. However, their role as antigens is not affected. The production of antibodies in the person receiving the vaccine is stimulated.	tetanus and diphtheria vaccines
a particular protein or small fragment of the pathogen	The protein or fragment acts as an antigen. Vaccines made in this way are called **subunit** vaccines. They avoid some of the side effects of whole vaccines.	human papilloma virus vaccine

Live attenuated vaccines are the most popular type of vaccine. Their advantages are that

• attenuated pathogens multiply in the person receiving the vaccine. Only a low dose of vaccine is therefore needed to deliver enough antigen for an effective immune reaction to occur

• live multiplying microorganisms stimulate the production of memory cells more effectively

However, their disadvantages are that

• mutation of the attenuated pathogen may make the vaccine ineffective or, very occasionally, the pathogen may revert to the disease-causing form

• live vaccines must be stored in cool conditions

How science works (L)

The discovery of vaccination

Edward Jenner (1749–1823) was a British country doctor who did not understand immunology as we do. But he was a good scientist who tested ideas formed from everyday experience.

He learnt from local farmers that milkmaids who caught the mild disease cowpox rarely caught the much more serious and often fatal disease smallpox. During an outbreak of smallpox in the neighbourhood, Jenner deliberately infected several of his patients with cowpox. The patients soon developed cowpox but were not affected by smallpox.

Jenner took the experiment a dangerous step further. He infected a boy who had just recovered from cowpox with pus from the spots of someone suffering from smallpox. The boy did not develop smallpox. His survival added weight to earlier ideas that giving a person a mild dose of a disease protects against more serious forms of the disease.

Jenner published his results in 1798 and the work established vaccination (immunization) as a powerful weapon in the fight against disease. At first people were suspicious and it took time for the technique to be accepted. Now smallpox has been eliminated from all parts of the world and vaccines protect millions of people from a variety of diseases.

Vaccination programmes

A vaccination programme coordinated by the World Health Organization worldwide helped to eradicate the deadly disease smallpox by 1977. As far as we know, smallpox virus exists only in secure laboratory facilities in the USA and Russia. Currently, there is debate as to whether or not these laboratory samples should be destroyed.

Other diseases such as rubella (German measles), polio, measles, and typhoid are far less common than before because of international vaccination programmes.

Mass vaccination breaks the chain of infection and makes it difficult for outbreaks of disease to occur and spread. The key to success is that most people are vaccinated – the so-called **herd effect**. However, the effect would soon disappear if the number of people vaccinated fell to levels where pathogens easily spread among unprotected individuals.

How science works (F)

The effectiveness of mass vaccination

Whooping cough vaccine is a suspension of killed *Bordetella pertussis*. It is usually given with diphtheria and tetanus vaccines in a **triple vaccine**.

Vaccination against whooping cough started in 1957. Before then about 100 000 cases of the disease were reported in the UK each year. By 1973 more than 80% of the population had been vaccinated and the number of annual cases fell to around 2400.

However, there was a scare over the safety of the vaccine and vaccinations fell to around 30% in 1975. Epidemics of whooping cough followed: there were nearly 66 000 cases in 1982 and more than 36 000 in 1986. Methods of producing the vaccine were improved.

A publicity campaign pointing out the advantages of vaccination helped to restore public confidence. The percentage of people vaccinated increased, halting further epidemics. In 1998 there were around 1500 cases of whooping cough reported in the UK; 95% of children had been vaccinated by the age of two years.

Monoclonal antibodies

White blood cells produce millions of antibodies to defend the body from attack by bacteria, viruses, fungi, and other potentially dangerous antigens. It is difficult to separate antibodies into pure samples of particular antibodies required to bind to specific antigens.

The problems can be overcome by fusing B cells that produce a particular antibody with a type of rapidly dividing lymphocyte cancer cell called a **myeloma**. The fused cells produce only the required antibody. Pure samples of antibodies made in this way are called **monoclonal antibodies**.

Monoclonal antibodies have a wide range of uses, including the treatment of some types of cancer. Cancer cells produce antigens different from those produced by healthy cells. Monoclonal antibodies that bind only to the abnormal antigens are used to target the cancer cells with drugs without affecting the healthy cells.

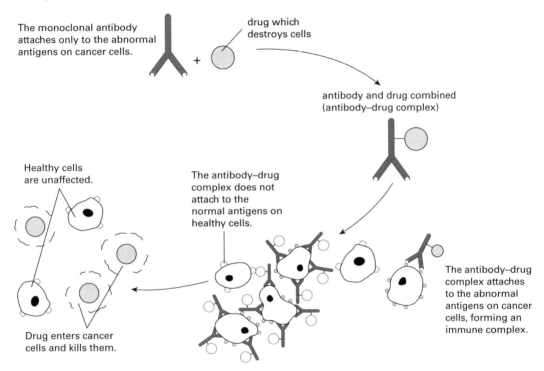

The monoclonal antibody attaches only to the abnormal antigens on cancer cells.

drug which destroys cells

antibody and drug combined (antibody–drug complex)

Healthy cells are unaffected.

The antibody–drug complex does not attach to the normal antigens on healthy cells.

The antibody–drug complex attaches to the abnormal antigens on cancer cells, forming an immune complex.

Drug enters cancer cells and kills them.

Using monoclonal antibodies to treat cancer

Monoclonal antibodies are also put to other uses.

- Monoclonal antibodies bind with poisons, inactivating them. Tetanus toxin and overdosage of digoxin (a drug used to treat heart disease) are inactivated using different types of monoclonal antibody.
- The success of transplants depends on matching the tissue of donor and patient as nearly as possible. The closer the match, the less chance there is of tissue rejection. Monoclonal antibodies, produced against the cell surface proteins of the donor's and patient's tissues, make tissue matching more accurate.

Developing different types of monoclonal antibody for medical and other uses is expensive. However, there are many new companies developing products in response to the demand.

Questions

1 What is a vaccine?
2 Explain the difference between active immunity and passive immunity.
3 What is the herd effect?
4 Summarize why monoclonal antibodies are used to treat some types of cancer.

2.00 HSW: Developing ideas of DNA

By the end of this section you should

○ *be able to analyse, interpret, and evaluate data concerning early experimental work relating to the role and importance of DNA.*

Before you start it will help to read sections **2.02** (DNA structure), **2.04** (chromosomes), and **2.10** (replication).

Discovering the chemical carrier of genetic information

1869   **Friedrich Miescher** identifies a substance in the pus soaking used surgical bandages. He calls the substance **nuclein** (now DNA) because it came from cell nuclei. The discovery arouses little interest.

1919   **Phoebus Levene** discovers the chemical make-up of nucleotides. He suggests that DNA consists of nucleotide units linked together through the phosphate groups.

1928   **Frederick Griffith** finds that the characteristics of 'smooth' *Pneumococcus* bacteria transfer to the 'rough' form of the same bacteria when live 'rough' bacteria are mixed with the killed 'smooth' form.

1937   **William Astbury** at Leeds University produces the first X-ray diffraction patterns showing that DNA has a regular structure.

1944   **Oswald Avery** and co-workers at the Rockefeller Institute identify the transforming principle discovered by Griffith as DNA.

1951   **Erwin Chargaff** at Columbia University finds that, in any sample of DNA, the amount of guanine is equal to the amount of cytosine and that the amount of adenine is equal to the amount of thymine. His discovery helps Watson and Crick establish the idea of complementary **base-pairing**.

1953   **Alfred Hershey** and **Martha Chase** show that DNA is the genetic material of T2 phage (a type of virus which infects bacteria).

1953   **James Watson** and **Francis Crick** in Cambridge propose that the structure of a molecule of DNA is a double helix, with two α-helical sugar and phosphate chains running on the outside linked by base pairs (adenine-thymine or guanine-cytosine) on the inside. They build a model of DNA which takes account of all the then-known features of DNA and which is their interpretation of the X-ray diffraction photographs of DNA taken by Rosalind Franklin at King's College London.

1958   **Matthew Meselson** and **Franklin Stahl** confirm the suggestion by Watson and Crick that DNA replication is semi-conservative. Each new molecule of double helix contains one strand of DNA from the original helix; the other strand forms as a complement of the original strand.

1961   **Francis Crick** and **Sydney Brenner** in Cambridge discover that triplets of bases (codons) each specify a particular amino acid unit in a polypeptide molecule.

1967   **Marshall Nirenberg** and co-workers establish that bacteria, amphibians, and mammals all share a common genetic code.

Question

1 Briefly summarize the contributions made by other scientists to the Watson-Crick model of the structure of DNA.

Our understanding of the importance of DNA has a long history. In 1953 the model by James Watson and Francis Crick proposing that the molecular structure of DNA is in the form of a double helix was an important turning point. Their discovery made possible the developments of molecular biology, which have revolutionized genetics. New discoveries in gene technology are bringing benefits to agriculture, industry, and medicine.

2.01   Variation and its causes

OBJECTIVES

By the end of the section you should

○ *be able to explain the difference between continuous and discontinuous variation*

○ *know the environmental causes of variation*

○ *understand the importance of random sampling, chance, and how to increase confidence in the conclusions drawn from biological studies*

○ *understand the genetic causes of variation: reshuffling genes, gene mutations, chromosome mutations*

Before you start it will help to read sections **2.03** (base sequences), **2.04** (chromosomes), **2.05** (meiosis), **2.10** (replication), and **2.18** (what is a species?)

If variation between individuals is so great that they are no longer varieties of the same species but different species, then the term 'interspecific variation' has little meaning. 'Intraspecific' and 'interspecific' referring to variation are terms little used.

Variation

The term **variation** refers to the differences that exist between individuals of the same species. For example variations in colour of eye, skin, hair, and shapes of face make us different from one another.

Continuous variation

Some characteristics show variations spread over a range of measurements. Height is an example. All *intermediate* heights are possible between one extreme (shortness) and the other (tallness). We say that the characteristic shows **continuous variation**.

The distribution curve shows that height varies about a mean which is typical for the species. This is the same for any other continuously variable characteristic of a species.

Characteristics which vary continuously are usually the result of the activity of numerous sets of genes. We say that they are **polygenic** in origin.

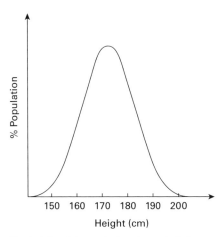

The height of the majority of people falls within the range 165–180 cm.

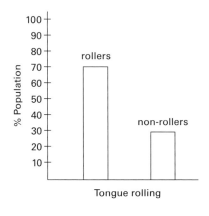

Tongue-rolling – an example of discontinuous variation

Discontinuous variation

Other characteristics do not show a spread of variation. There are no intermediate forms but distinct categories. For example most human blood groups are either A, B, AB, or O; pea plants are either tall or short (dwarf). We say that the characteristics show **discontinuous variation**.

Notice in the bar chart that some people can roll the tongue, others cannot. There are no intermediate half-rollers!

Characteristics which vary discontinuously are usually the result of the activity of one set of genes. We say that they are **monogenic** in origin.

What is standard deviation?

The distribution curve of human height has a 'middle': the apex of the graph where the height of the largest percentage of the population is identified. The value of the 'middle' is called the **mean**. (Other measures of 'middleness' are the median and the mode, but the mean is most usually used.)

When comparing means, it is useful to know the extent to which the data is 'spread out' around each mean. The **standard deviation** is the most usual measure of 'spread-outness'.

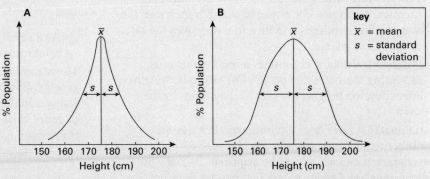

Standard deviation. The mean of each distribution curve of human population is the same. However the value of the standard deviation about each mean is different. The difference shows that the variation in height of population B is greater than in population A.

Significant differences and drawing conclusions

When comparing means, it is very unlikely that they will be the same. Each mean is the average of a set of data consisting of different readings. We can never be absolutely sure of any conclusions made from comparing the means of data sets. The conclusions are **tentative** (not definitive).

However, appropriate statistical tests help us to judge if the compared means are really different from one another or that any differences are just due to chance. Most biological studies set a **confidence level** of 95% or better that the means are really different from one another. If the results meet this confidence level, then we say that the means are **significantly different**.

Sampling

An environment and the organisms living in it form an **ecosystem**. A forest is an example. Ecological studies are designed to investigate different ecosystems, but most are far too large to study all that is there. Instead, scientists investigate selected parts called **samples** and assume that these are representative of the ecosystem as a whole.

An investigation is designed to take samples at random. **Random sampling** means that any part of the ecosystem (its physical environment/organisms) has an equal chance of being sampled. Different methods are used to ensure random sampling, such as using tables of random numbers to select samples.

Random sampling avoids bias in the data gathered during any investigation. Biased data might lead to false conclusions.

Environmental causes of variation

Variation arises from environmental causes. Here 'environmental' means of all of the external influences affecting an organism. Examples are:

- **Nutrients** in the food we eat and minerals that plants absorb in solution through the roots. For example, in many countries children are now taller and heavier, age for age, than they were 50 or more years ago because of improved diet and standards of living.
- **Drugs** which may have a serious effect on appearance. For example, thalidomide was given to pregnant women to prevent then feeling sick and help them sleep. The drug can affect development of the fetus and some women prescribed thalidomide gave birth to seriously deformed children.
- **Temperature** affects the rate of enzyme-controlled chemical reactions. For example, warmth increases the rate of photosynthesis and therefore improves the rate of growth of plants.
- **Physical training** uses muscles more than normal, increasing their size and power. For example, weight-lifters develop bulging muscles as they train for their sport.

Variations that arise from environmental causes are not inherited because sex cells are not affected. Instead the characteristics are said to be **acquired**. Because the weight-lifter has developed bulging muscles does not mean that his/her children will have bulging muscles unless they take up weight-lifting as well!

Genetic causes of variation

Genetic causes and environmental causes of variation affect the structure and function of individuals. But *only* variations arising from genetic causes are inherited.

Reshuffling genes

- During meiosis, homologous chromosomes pair and then **segregate** (separate) into daughter cells following cytokinesis. The paired chromosomes segregate independently of each other. The process is called **independent assortment**.
  - As a result the sex cells (gametes) produced vary genetically, depending on the combination of chromosomes in each daughter cell.
  - As a result of random mating, parental genes are recombined in new arrangements in the **zygote** (fertilized egg).
  - As a result offspring are genetically different (vary) from each other and from their parents (except identical twins, which are genetically the same).
- Crossing over in a bivalent may involve each pair of chromatids:

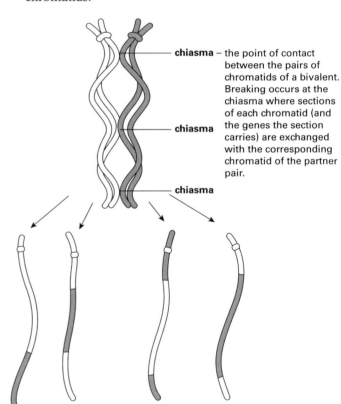

chiasma – the point of contact between the pairs of chromatids of a bivalent. Breaking occurs at the chiasma where sections of each chromatid (and the genes the section carries) are exchanged with the corresponding chromatid of the partner pair.

Crossing over produces many recombinations of genes.

  - As a result very large numbers of recombinations of chromatids (and therefore genes) are possible.
- The recombination of chromosomes (and therefore genes) following crossing over may result in major changes in the organism's genome. The activity of genes varies depending on their location on a chromosome.
  - As a result new proteins are produced.

Mutations

The term **mutation** refers to an alteration in the arrangement or the amount of the genetic material of a cell.

- Mutations that occur in sex cells (sperm or eggs) are **inherited by** (passed on to) subsequent generations.
- Those that occur in the other (body) cells of the organism are not passed on. These mutations are called **somatic** mutations.

Gene mutations occur when the sequence of bases is incorrectly copied during DNA replication. Nucleotides (and their bases) may be

- inserted – bases are added
- deleted – bases are lost
- duplicated – bases are repeated
- inverted – bases are turned round
- substituted – bases are copied wrongly

The mutation may result in a new order in which amino acids are assembled, resulting in an error in the synthesis of protein. If only a single base is involved then the gene mutation is called a **point mutation**.

Chromosome mutations occur when chromosomes break in the early stages of meiosis. Normally breakage is followed by **crossing-over** and new combinations of genes are produced. Variation is increased.

However breakage of chromosomes may have other consequences:

- deletion – a chromosome or part of a chromosome is lost
- translocation – the broken part of a chromosome joins to another chromosome
- inversion – the broken part of a chromosome rejoins the chromosome but after turning through 180°

Another type of chromosome mutation is caused by the gain or loss of one or more whole chromosomes. For example a particular pair of homologous chromosomes may not separate during meiosis but instead together pass into the same cell, a phenomenon called **non-disjunction**. Two sorts of sex cell are produced: one sort does not have any copies of the chromosome in question, the other sort has two.

- Fusion of a sex cell that has two copies of a chromosome with a normal sex cell (fertilization) results in a zygote with three copies of that chromosome: a condition called **trisomy**.
- Fusion of a sex cell that has no copies of the chromosome with a sex cell that has the normal single copy gives rise to a fetus whose body cells each have only one of that chromosome.

The diagram shows the possible outcomes in a human fetus where non-disjunction of chromosome number 21 occurs during meiosis in one parent. The resulting trisomy is referred to as **Down's syndrome**. The affected individual has an extra copy of chromosome 21 in each body cell.

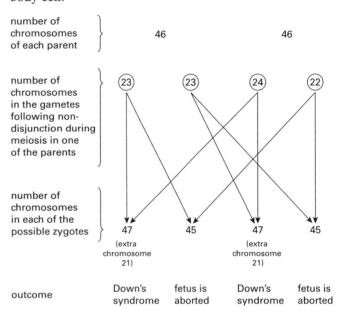

Trisomy 21 may lead to a fetus with Down's syndrome.

Remember :

- Normally sex cells are haploid: each cell has only one copy of each of the chromosomes that make up the genetic material of the cell.
- Body (**somatic**) cells are normally diploid: each cell has two copies of each chromosome.

Fact file

Mutations change the base sequences of genes. A new sequence may carry information which enables cells to synthesize molecules of a polypeptide. However, the sequence and type of amino acids which make up the new polypeptide might be different from the polypeptide encoded by the original gene. The difference(s) might mean that the polypeptide does not work properly (it is non-functional). If the non-functional polypeptide is an enzyme then the chemical reactions which the enzyme usually catalyse do not take place.

Questions

1. Explain the difference between a characteristic which shows continuous variation and one that shows discontinuous variation.

2. Data is often represented by its mean and standard deviation. Explain the relationship between them.

3. Why are genetic causes of variation inherited and environmental causes not inherited?

4. List the different ways gene mutations occur.

2.02 Structure of DNA

By the end of the section you should

○ *know the structure of a nucleotide*

○ *know that DNA is a polynucleotide made of many nucleotides joined together*

○ *understand that the structure of DNA is in the form of a double helix held together by hydrogen bonding between its bases*

Before you start, it will help to read sections **2.00** (discovery of DNA) and **2.10** (DNA replication).

Deoxyribonucleic acid (DNA) is a nucleic acid. Its molecules contain the genetic information which instructs cells to synthesize (make) **ribonucleic acid (RNA** – another type of nucleic acid) and proteins.

'Genetic' means that the information is inherited (passed on to) by daughter cells when parent cells divide.

• The sections of DNA that carry genetic information are called **genes**.
• Other sections of DNA control the use of this genetic information.

Nucleotides

DNA is made up of monomers called **nucleotides**. A nucleotide in the case of DNA has three components – a molecule each of

• the pentose sugar **deoxyribose**
• a **base** which is either **adenine (A)**, **thymine (T)**, **guanine (G)**, or **cytosine (C)**
• a **phosphate** group

Condensation reactions join the components together forming a nucleotide.

Structure of a nucleotide

DNA structure

Many condensation reactions join together nucleotide units forming a strand of DNA.

Notice in the diagram

• Adjacent sugar rings join through the phosphate group from carbon atom 3 of one sugar to carbon atom 5 of the next sugar in line.
• These links are **phosphodiester** bonds and hold the DNA strand together.

A shorthand way of describing this linkage is $3' \rightarrow 5' \rightarrow 3'$.

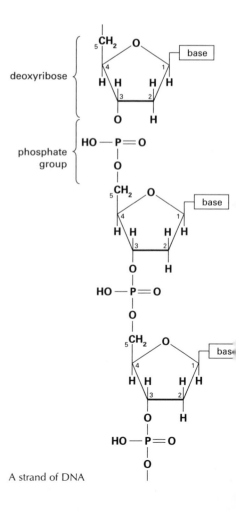

A strand of DNA

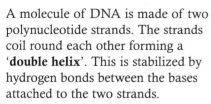

A molecule of DNA is made of two polynucleotide strands. The strands coil round each other forming a '**double helix**'. This is stabilized by hydrogen bonds between the bases attached to the two strands.

Notice in the diagram:

- A only bonds with T
- G only bonds with C

This arrangement is called **complementary base pairing**.

ℝ As a result, all of the information in the double-stranded sequence of bases of a DNA molecule is duplicated on each strand.

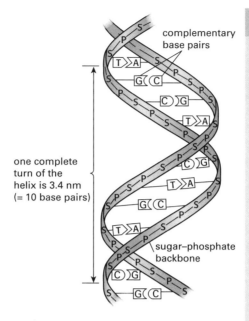

one complete turn of the helix is 3.4 nm (= 10 base pairs)

complementary base pairs

sugar–phosphate backbone

key

S = deoxyribose sugar
P = phosphate sugar
A, T, G, C = different bases

The double helix structure of DNA

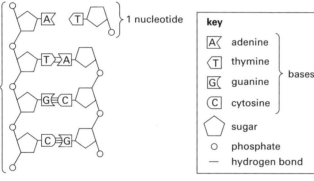

strand formed by alternate sugar and phosphate molecules

1 nucleotide

key

A	adenine	
T	thymine	bases
G	guanine	
C	cytosine	

⬠ sugar
○ phosphate
— hydrogen bond

Complementary base pairing in DNA

Notice in the diagram above:

- one strand runs from carbon atom $3' \rightarrow 5' \rightarrow 3'$... and so on in one direction
- its partner strand runs $5' \rightarrow 3' \rightarrow 5'$ in the opposite direction

We say that the strands are **anti-parallel**.

The hydrogen bonds linking bases are sufficiently strong and numerous to hold together a molecule of nucleic acid. But they are also weak enough to break during DNA replication or when genetic information is being transcribed.

How science works (C)

Discovering the structure of DNA

By the 1950s, it was recognized that DNA is the genetic material of cells. Discovering its structure was a priority and different techniques were used to solve the problem. Success came in 1953 when James Watson and Francis Crick combined all the evidence from different sources. They succeeded in building a model of DNA which fitted all of the known facts.

At the time Rosalind Franklin was using X-ray crystallography to probe the arrangement of the atoms of DNA molecules. The technique involved focusing a beam of X-rays through a fibre of DNA on to a photographic plate.

- X-rays affect photographic emulsion. A pattern of dots can be seen when the plate is developed.
- The pattern of dots represents the position of the atoms making up the molecule.
- Plotting the density of the dots (and therefore of the atoms) and their spatial relationships allows the information in the pattern to be interpreted as a 3D model of the molecule.

Franklin's work played a key role in solving the problem of the structure of DNA.

Questions

1 What does the term 'genetic' mean?
2 Briefly explain the relationship between phosphodiester bonds, complementary base pairing, and a molecule of double-stranded DNA.
3 What are the components of a nucleotide?

2.03 Genes and polypeptides

OBJECTIVES

By the end of the section you should

○ be able to explain that some sections of a strand of DNA specify the sequence of amino acid units that form a polypeptide

○ know that the section of DNA specifying a particular polypeptide is called a gene

○ understand that the triplet of nucleotides which specifies the position of a particular amino acid unit in a polypeptide is called a codon

○ understand that not all nuclear DNA codes for polypeptides

Before you start, it will help to read section **1.04** (amino acids and peptide bonds) and **2.01** (mutations and base sequences).

Remember that a strand of DNA may consist of thousands of nucleotides joined together. Each nucleotide has a base (A, T, C, or G) as part of its structure. A strand of DNA, therefore, carries a sequence (a particular order) of bases.

Fact file

We say that the genetic code is **degenerate** because nearly all of the amino acids are each coded for by more than one codon.

Of the 64 possible codons:

• three are stop codons – during protein synthesis 'stop' means 'end of polypeptide chain'

• one codon is an 'initiator' – during protein synthesis this means 'start of polypeptide chain'

Genes

Some sections of strands of DNA carry information which enables cells to synthesize (make) molecules of polypeptide. The information is carried in the sequence of bases on the nucleotides which make up these sections. The sections are called **genes**.

The differences between genes are the result of differences in the sequences of their bases.

Estimates suggest that most human cells each carry 20 000 to 30 000 genes, enabling the cells to synthesize millions of different types of polypeptide.

Genes are often categorized as:

• **structural genes** – affecting the synthesis of enzymes and the other polypeptides that make up body structures. For example collagen accounts for up to 25% of total body protein (tendons, ligaments, connective tissue, etc.)

• **regulatory genes** – affecting the synthesis of polypeptides which control the development of organism. Regulatory genes may also affect the activity of other genes.

The term **locus** refers to the position of a gene on a particular strand of DNA. The ordered list of gene loci (plural of locus) is called a **genetic map**.

The genetic code

To make a molecule of a particular polypeptide, many amino acid units must combine in the correct order. The sequence of bases of a gene is responsible for getting the order correct. In other words, the sequence carries the information which enables a cell to assemble that particular polypeptide.

The sequence of bases of all of the genes of a cell, and the information each sequence carries, is the **genetic code**. The code is almost universal. It is the same in the cells of most living things.

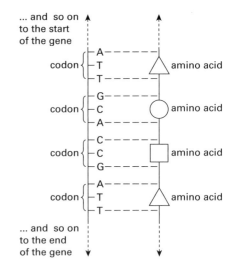

The information needed to assemble one amino acid unit in its correct place in a polypeptide is contained in a sequence of three bases. The sequence is called a **codon**. A gene therefore is a sequence of codons and the genetic code is all of the codons in the DNA of a cell.

Each triplet code in a gene forms a codon for a particular amino acid. The sequence of codons controls the sequence of amino acids in a polypeptide.

Coding and non-coding DNA

In eukaryotes most genes are not a continuous sequence of codons. Non-coding regions (called **introns**) split up the coding regions (called **exons**).

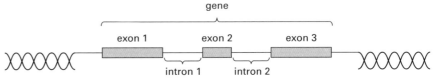

A gene is usually a sequence of exons and introns.

Also there are non-coding regions of DNA between genes. These non-coding regions often consist of short sequences of bases which repeat over and over again (multiple repeats) and are called **mini-satellites**.

Questions

1 What is a gene?

2 Why is the genetic code described as a triplet code?

3 What does the term 'locus' mean?

2.04   DNA and chromosomes

O B J E C T I V E S

By the end of the section you should understand

○ *that in eukaryotic cells (a) DNA molecules are usually linear, and (b) DNA is associated with proteins called histones*

○ *that in prokaryotic cells (a) DNA molecules are often looped and smaller than those in eukaryotic cells, and (b) DNA molecules are associated with other types of protein (not histones)*

○ *that the association of DNA with different types of protein forms chromosomes.*

Before you start, it will help to read sections **2.10** (replication) and **2.11** (mitosis).

Chromosomes

The bar-shaped structures seen in an optical microscope when the nucleus of a eukaryotic cell divides are its **chromosomes**. Each chromosome consists of:

- a single length of DNA which carries many genes
- proteins called **histones** which bind to the DNA, packaging it and controlling its functions

During interphase chromosomes are not seen as individual structures in the optical microscope. They exist in condensed form as a tangled mix of DNA and protein called **chromatin**.

The visible structure of chromosomes

In the early stages of mitosis and meiosis, strands of chromatin condense and become more compact, forming individual chromosomes. The chromosomes strongly take up some types of stain. For example, Feulgen's stain colours the chromosome a deep purple, making them easily seen in the optical microscope.

A chromosome is usually seen as a four-arm structure, consisting of a pair of **chromatids** and a **centromere**.

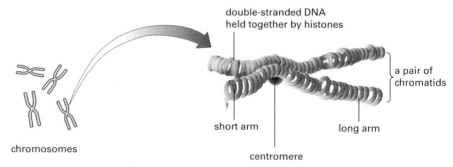

Chromosome structure

Notice that each chromatid consists of a short arm and a long arm.

- Each chromatid is one of the two identical parts of the chromosome formed after DNA replication during the S-phase of interphase.
- The centromere is the point where the two chromatids touch and which attach to the microtubules of the spindle fibres formed during prophase and metaphase.

What is a chromosome?

The term 'chromosome' not only refers to the four-arm structures visible during division of the eukaryotic nucleus. It also refers to the small looped DNA molecules called **plasmids** found in prokaryotic cells.

 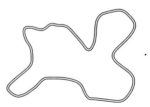

Plasmid structure

Looped DNA is also found in yeast cells, the mitochondria of plant and animal cells, and in the chloroplasts of plant cells.

Viruses contain the simplest chromosomes. In those containing DNA, the molecules are short lengths or loops and often not associated with any proteins.

Questions

1 What do the chromosomes of a eukaryotic cell each consist of?

2 Briefly explain the relationship between a chromosome and a pair of chromatids.

3 What is a plasmid?

2.05 Meiosis

OBJECTIVES

By the end of the section you should

○ *know that meiosis is a type of cell division that produces haploid gametes*

○ *understand that homologous chromosomes segregate independently during meiosis*

○ *understand that crossing over reshuffles genes producing new combinations*

Before you start, it will help to read sections **2.10** (replication) and **2.11** (mitosis).

Fact file

Only the cells that give rise to gametes (the sex cells) divide by **meiosis**. Sex cells are produced in the sex organs:

• the **testes** of the male and **ovaries** of the female in mammals

• the **anthers** (male) and the **carpels** (female) in flowering plants.

Remember that during cell division the chromosomes in the nucleus of the **parent** cell pass to the new **daughter** cells. 'Daughter' does not mean that the cells are female. It means that they are the new cells formed as a result of cell division.

Remember that, strictly, meiosis (and mitosis) refers to the processes which lead to the division of the nucleus of the parent cell. **Cytokinesis** which follows meiosis (and mitosis) describes division of the cell itself.

Cell division by meiosis gives rises to gametes (sex cells). It progresses through the same phases as mitosis (with some differences), but the phases occur twice over.

• The first meiotic division is a **reduction** division which results in two daughter cells, each with half the number of chromosomes of the nucleus of the parent cell. The cells are haploid.

• The second meiotic division is a mitosis during which the two haploid daughter cells (resulting from the first meiotic division) divide.

Daughter cells which are haploid rather than diploid are an important difference which distinguishes meiosis from mitosis.

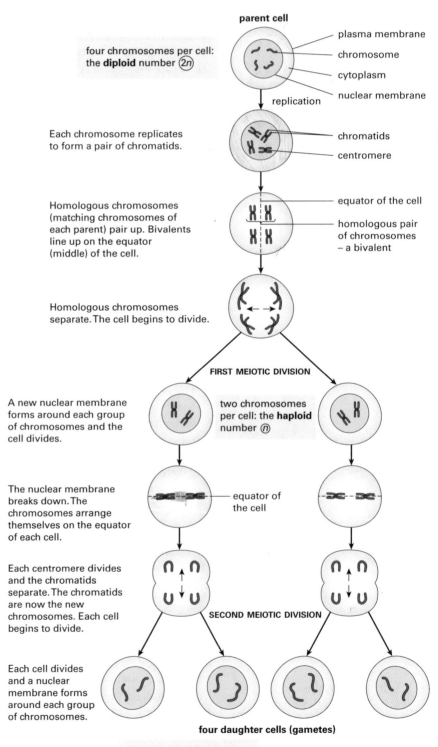

parent cell

plasma membrane
chromosome
cytoplasm
nuclear membrane

four chromosomes per cell: the **diploid** number ②

replication

Each chromosome replicates to form a pair of chromatids.

chromatids
centromere

Homologous chromosomes (matching chromosomes of each parent) pair up. Bivalents line up on the equator (middle) of the cell.

equator of the cell
homologous pair of chromosomes – a bivalent

Homologous chromosomes separate. The cell begins to divide.

FIRST MEIOTIC DIVISION

A new nuclear membrane forms around each group of chromosomes and the cell divides.

two chromosomes per cell: the **haploid** number ⑩

The nuclear membrane breaks down. The chromosomes arrange themselves on the equator of each cell.

equator of the cell

Each centromere divides and the chromatids separate. The chromatids are now the new chromosomes. Each cell begins to divide.

SECOND MEIOTIC DIVISION

Each cell divides and a nuclear membrane forms around each group of chromosomes.

four daughter cells (gametes)

Meiosis occurs in two phases. The resulting gametes have half the number of chromosomes of the parent cell.

two chromosomes per cell: the **haploid** number ⑩

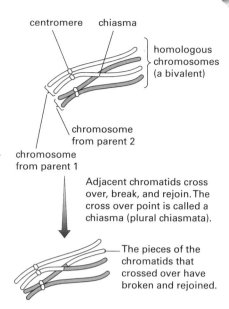

centremere   chiasma

homologous chromosomes (a bivalent)

chromosome from parent 2

chromosome from parent 1

Adjacent chromatids cross over, break, and rejoin. The cross over point is called a chiasma (plural chiasmata).

The pieces of the chromatids that crossed over have broken and rejoined.

Crossing over results in new combinations of genes (gene recombination) on the chromatids.

The importance of meiosis

- Daughter cells each receive a half (**haploid** or *n*) set of chromosomes from the parent cell.
  - ℝ As a result, during **fertilization** (when sperm and egg join together) the chromosomes of each cell combine.
  - ℝ As a result, the **zygote** (fertilized egg) receives a full (**diploid** or *2n*) set of chromosomes, but inherits a new combination of the genes carried on the chromosomes (50:50) from the parents.
  - ℝ As a result, the new individual inherits characteristics from both parents, not just from one parent as in asexual reproduction.

What is the result of meiosis?

- The diploid number of chromosomes has been halved. In the diagrams, the diploid number 4 is halved to 2.
- Genetic material is exchanged between homologous chromosomes (as a result of crossing over).
- Chromosomes separate randomly.
  - ℝ As a result alleles (genes) are separated randomly – a process called **independent assortment**.
  - ℝ As a result male (paternal) and female (maternal) chromosomes are distributed randomly among the daughter cells.

Meiosis generates genetic variation

The diagram shows two pairs of chromosomes of a **sperm mother cell** (a cell which gives rise to sperm). Each chromosome is represented as a **bivalent** along which are located the genes AA, aa, BB, bb, CC, cc, DD, dd.

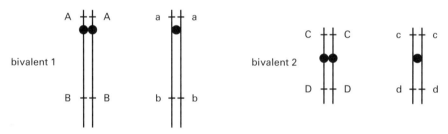

If there is only *one* crossover in each bivalent, then the possible genotypes of the sperm produced by the sperm mother cell can be mapped. The diagram shows the possible combinations of genes.

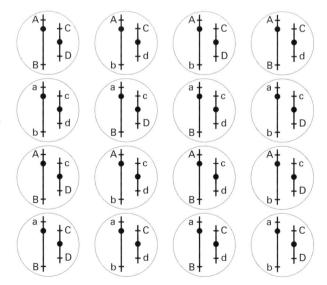

These two bivalents with one crossover can produce 16 combinations.

Human cells each (except red blood cells and gametes) have 23 pairs of chromosomes – the equivalent of 92 bivalents. In each bivalent more than one crossover can occur, potentially generating an enormous variety of genetic combinations.

Questions

1 In what tissues does meiosis take place in mammals and flowering plants?

2 Explain the importance of meiosis.

3 What is the result of meiosis?

2.06 Genetic diversity

Differences in DNA within a gene pool

Genetic diversity is represented by the variation in the genetic material of members of a population.

- Differences between population members can be due to differences in the base sequences of the sections of DNA which form their genes. The differences arise as a result of gene mutations.
- Differences in chromosomes can arise as a result of:
  (a) crossing over and independent assortment during meiosis
  (b) the recombination of parental chromosomes in the zygote
- Whole genomes can vary as a result of differences in the base sequences of the non-coding DNA. The differences in the base sequences of non-coding DNA are also the result of mutations.

Think of a population not as a group of individuals each with a set of genes, but as a pool of genes. **Gene flow** within a **gene pool** refers to the transfer of parental genes to offspring when parents reproduce sexually.

Unrestricted gene flow maximizes genetic diversity within the gene pool. Each member of the population has the same chance as any other member of mating with an individual of the opposite sex and contributing its genes to the gene pool.

Changing genetic diversity

Restriction of gene flow reduces the size of the gene pool. In effect, the size of the population whose members can freely mate is reduced.

The frequency of genes in the gene pool of the smaller population is often different from the original larger population. The genetic diversity of small populations is therefore different from that of larger populations.

The founder effect and genetic bottleneck

The term **founder effect** refers to the change in genetic diversity in a small group of individuals compared with the genetic diversity of the larger population from which the group has separated.

The frequency of genes in the gene pool formed by the founder individuals of the small group may not be representative of the frequency of genes in the larger population from which the founder individuals have come.

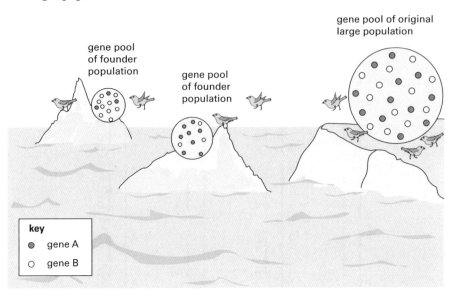

The founder effect. The frequency of genes A and B is different in the founder populations on each of the islands, and different from the original population.

The diagram illustrates how the founder effect may influence the evolution of founder populations.

- The frequency of the genes in the gene pools is different from each other and from the frequency of the genes in the gene pool of the original population.
  - As a result the effects of natural selection will cause the founder populations to diverge quickly.
- Eventually, the founder populations give rise to new species.

A **genetic bottleneck** forms when a previously large population is so reduced in numbers that only a few individuals survive.

- Like founder populations, the frequency of the genes in the gene pool of survivors is likely to be different from the frequency of genes in the gene pool of the original much larger population.
- Providing the surviving population does not become extinct, the individuals from any later increase in numbers will inherit a different frequency of genes compared with the population before the bottleneck occurred.

Research shows that founder events (whether by establishing new colonies or bottlenecks) are not likely to reduce genetic variation, unless the number of founders is very small (a single pregnant female for example). However the frequency of genes in founder populations is often different from the original population from where the founders originate.

Selective breeding

Selective breeding reduces the number of different genes in the populations of crops and domesticated animals raised for food.

- The development of high yielding breeds of domesticated animals and strains of plants has reduced genetic diversity in their populations.
  - As a result the members of a population are genetically similar.
- Should the conditions in which the animals and crops are raised alter in the future, the selective breeding of new varieties able to survive the changed conditions may not be possible because there is a smaller pool of genes to draw from.

The reduction of genetic diversity and the limitations this might bring to the selection of new varieties of crops and domesticated animals are some of the ethical issues involved in selective breeding programmes.

Selective breeding produces varieties of dogs which may look very different from one another. However, the different varieties all belong to the same species and genetically are very similar.

How science works (I)

In 1845 the most popular variety of potato grown in Ireland was the *Lumper*. Similar in appearance and genetic make-up to the original varieties from Peru, the *Lumper* was partly responsible for the increase in Ireland's population during the first part of the nineteenth century. It produces excellent yields and provided a staple part of the diet for many years.

However, the *Lumper* has a fatal genetic flaw which no-one at the time was aware of. It is a late maincrop variety which is particularly susceptible to blight – a fungus (*Phytophthera infestans*) – which was then unknown in Ireland.

Cool wet weather in July 1845 provided the ideal conditions for the spread of potato blight spores. Blight devastated the crop of *Lumper* potatoes, and by 1847 the Irish potato harvest had failed completely.

The rapidly growing human population depended on this one type of food, so the blight resulted in widespread famine. More than a million people died of starvation. A further million escaped famine by emigrating, mainly to the USA. Within a few years the population of Ireland was halved.

The European potato industry was founded on varieties from tubers brought from Peru to Spain in the 1570s and to England around 1590. Since then cross-breeding has mixed up the genes contained in the original introductions and recombined them into new varieties. Breeders and growers have then selected those varieties with the most promising characteristics. However, even modern varieties are all rather similar genetically as they all rely on the limited number of original genes.

Questions

1 What does the phrase 'genetic diversity' mean?

2 What is the difference between gene flow and a gene pool?

3 Explain the relationship between the founder effect and a genetic bottleneck.

2.07 Haemoglobin

OBJECTIVES

By the end of the section you should

○ *know that haemoglobin is a globular protein with a quaternary structure*

○ *understand the role of haemoglobin in the transport of oxygen*

○ *be able to interpret the oxygen dissociation curve and the effects of carbon dioxide concentration on it*

○ *know that different types of haemoglobin are suited to particular ways of life.*

Before you start, it will help to read section **1.04** (quaternary structure).

The haemoglobin molecule

Haemoglobin is the oxygen-carrying pigment in red blood cells. It is a **globular** protein with a quaternary structure, consisting of

- four coiled polypeptide chains (the **globin** part of the molecule)
- four **haem** groups

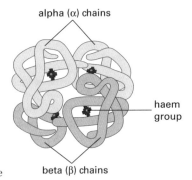

alpha (α) chains

haem group

beta (β) chains

The haemoglobin molecule

> Most enzymes, antibodies, and some hormones are globular proteins made of polypeptide chains that fold into a spherical shape. They are usually soluble in water.

Each haem group is a **prosthetic group** – part of the protein but not made of amino acids.

- The four haem groups each contain an iron ion that can combine with a molecule of oxygen.
  - Ⓡ As a result a molecule of haemoglobin can combine with four molecules of oxygen.

$$H_2C=CH \quad H \quad CH_3 \quad CH_2$$
$$H_3C \quad \quad CH$$
$$N \quad N$$
$$H \quad Fe \quad H$$
$$N \quad N$$
$$H_3C \quad \quad CH_3$$
$$H_2C-CH_2 \quad H \quad H_2C-CH_2$$
$$^-OOC \quad \quad COO^-$$

A haem group of haemoglobin

Haemoglobin transports oxygen

Oxygen combines with haemoglobin forming **oxyhaemoglobin** in tissues where the concentration of oxygen is high. It quickly releases its oxygen in tissues where the concentration of oxygen is low.

Haemoglobin is therefore ideal for the transport of oxygen from the lungs (where the concentration of oxygen is high) to the rest of the body's tissues (where the concentration of oxygen may be low).

$$\text{haemoglobin} + \text{oxygen} \underset{\text{other body tissues}}{\overset{\text{lungs}}{\rightleftharpoons}} \text{oxyhaemoglobin}$$

- Blood which contains a lot of oxyhaemoglobin is called **oxygenated** blood and is bright red.
- Blood with less oxyhaemoglobin in it is called **deoxygenated** blood and looks red/purple.

Uptake of oxygen and the dissociation curve

The partial pressure (in kPa) of a gas is a measure of its concentration. It is proportional to its percentage by volume in a mixture of gases.

- The atmosphere contains nearly 21% oxygen. The partial pressure of oxygen is therefore about 21 kPa.
- The combination of haemoglobin with oxygen depends on the partial pressure of oxygen in contact with it.

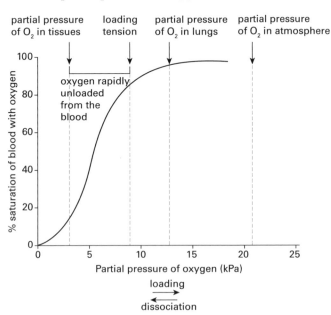

Oxygen association/dissociation curve for adult haemoglobin

Reading the graph from left to right shows the relationship between the *uptake* of oxygen by haemoglobin (association) and the increasing partial pressure (concentration) of oxygen in contact with it.

Notice:

- Haemoglobin takes up oxygen rapidly for a relatively small increase in the partial pressure of the gas. The term **loading tension** refers to the point when 95% of the pigment is saturated.

- The loading tension corresponds to a partial pressure which is considerably less than the partial pressure of oxygen in the atmosphere.

  ℝ As a result the blood supplying the lungs becomes rapidly loaded with oxygen at the partial pressure of oxygen normally found in the lungs.

Reading the graph from right to left shows the relationship between the *release* of oxygen by haemoglobin (dissociation) and the decreasing partial pressure of oxygen in contact with it.

Notice:

- Haemoglobin releases (unloads) oxygen rapidly for a relatively small decrease in partial pressure of the gas.
- The unloading of oxygen corresponds to a partial pressure of oxygen normally found is tissues which are using oxygen in aerobic respiration.

  ℝ As a result tissues receive enough oxygen for their activities.

What makes the dissociation curve S-shaped?

Remember that a haemoglobin molecule combines with four molecules of oxygen.

- The combination of oxygen with one haem group slightly changes the shape of the haemoglobin molecule.
- The shape change makes it easier for one of the other haem groups to load an oxygen molecule.
- The combination of oxygen with this haem group makes it even easier for a third haem group to load oxygen, and so on.

The S-shape of the dissociation curve is the result of these knock-on effects.

The effects work in reverse:

- As the partial pressure of oxygen decreases, an oxygen molecule may be released.
- Its loss slightly changes the shape of the haemoglobin molecule, making the unloading of subsequent oxygen molecules increasingly easy.

How do the loading and unloading properties of haemoglobin help with oxygen transport?

The partial pressure of oxygen in the lungs is about 12 kPa. In the tissues the partial pressure of oxygen is much lower – 2 kPa in muscle tissue for example. Haemoglobin exposed to this concentration of oxygen is less than 20% saturated. The oxygen released from the haemoglobin molecules passes into the blood plasma, diffuses into the muscle cells and is used in aerobic respiration.

The Bohr effect

- Reducing the partial pressure of carbon dioxide *increases* the oxygen load of the blood for a given partial pressure of oxygen.

- Increasing the partial pressure of carbon dioxide *reduces* the oxygen load of the blood for a given partial pressure of oxygen.
- Increasing temperature has a similar effect.

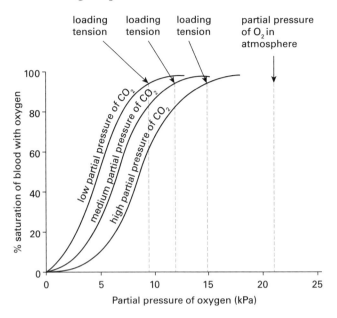

The more its dissociation curve is shifted to the right, the *less* readily haemoglobin loads oxygen, and the *more* readily it releases it. The more the curve is shifted to the left, the *more* readily haemoglobin loads oxygen and the *less* readily it releases it.

These alterations in the oxygen dissociation curve (called the **Bohr effect**) help to adjust the amount of oxygen tissues receive. For example, the demand for oxygen by muscle tissues during vigorous exercise is high. As the tissues respire more and more carbon dioxide is released. The temperature of the tissues also increases. These changes in the micro-environment of the tissues cause the dissociation curve to shift to the right, increasing the supply of oxygen to the tissues at a time when it is needed.

Different types of haemoglobin

Vertebrates (fish, amphibia, reptiles, birds, and mammals), some insects, and many types of worm have different types of haemoglobin in their blood. Differences between the various molecules include variations in:

- the structure of polypeptide chains
- the number of polypeptide chains
- the number of haem groups

The lugworm *Arenicola* lives in mud burrows in the intertidal zone of the seashore. The concentration of oxygen in its burrow is low between tides. The dissociation curve of its haemoglobin is shifted to the left. This means that the haemoglobin will still load oxygen even at low concentration. It only gives up oxygen when concentrations drop to very low levels, enabling *Arenicola* to survive when its burrow is uncovered at low tide.

Questions

1 Why is haemoglobin described as a globular protein with a quaternary structure?

2 When does the oxygen dissociation curve become an oxygen association curve?

3 How are different types of haemoglobin suited to particular ways of life?

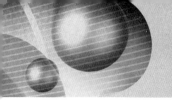

2.08 Starch, glycogen, and cellulose

By the end of the section you should

○ *recall that molecules of α glucose and β glucose are isomers, and that a molecule of polysaccharide is formed from condensation reactions between many molecules of monosaccharide*

○ *understand that the properties of starch, glycogen, and cellulose (different polysaccharides) affect their functions in cells*

Before you start, it will help to read section **1.06** (carbohydrates).

Molecular structures

Recall that the –OH (hydroxyl) group on carbon atom 1 of an α glucose molecule is *below* the plane of the ring of carbon atoms. In β glucose it is *above* the plane.

α glucose   **β glucose**

Starch

Starch is a polysaccharide formed from condensation reactions between many molecules of α glucose. It has two components:

- **amylose** – consists of unbranched chains of α 1–4 glycosidic bonds between α glucose molecules. Each chain coils like a spiral staircase into a helical structure.

amylose

glucose units

α 1–4 linkage

- **amylopectin** – consists of branched chains with 1–6 glycosidic bonds between α glucose molecules forming the branches

α 1–6 linkage

α 1–4 linkage

glucose units

side branch

main branch

amylopectin

Glycogen

Glycogen is like amylopectin except that it consists of
- fewer 1–4 glycosidic bonds between α glucose molecules
- many more 1–6 linkages

Cellulose

Cellulose is formed from condensation reactions between many molecules of β glucose.

- The –OH (hydroxyl) group on carbon atom 1 is *above* the plane of the ring of carbon atoms.
- The –OH group on carbon atom 4 is *below* the plane of the ring.
  - As a result, for the –OH groups on carbon atoms 1 and 4 of adjacent β glucose molecules to form a glycosidic bond, one molecule has to be flipped over (rotated through 180°) relative to its next-door neighbour:

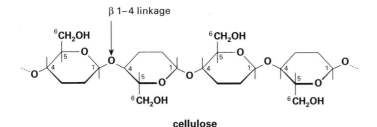

cellulose

The formation of β 1–4 glycosidic linkages produces rigid chain-like molecules.

- **Hydrogen bonds** cross-link chains into bundles called **microfibrils**.
- Further hydrogen bonding bind microfibrils into **fibres**.

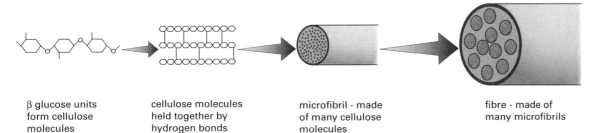

| β glucose units form cellulose molecules | cellulose molecules held together by hydrogen bonds | microfibril - made of many cellulose molecules | fibre - made of many microfibrils |

Cellulose has a tightly bundled structure.

Food stores

Starch and glycogen are almost insoluble which means that they have little effect on the osmotic properties of cells. Therefore they can be stored in cells as energy reserves.

- Starch is stored in plant cells.
- Glycogen is stored in animal cells.

Enzyme-catalysed reactions break down starch and glycogen into glucose. When glucose is oxidized, energy is released and carbon dioxide and water formed. The term **cellular respiration** refers to the series of reactions.

Structural materials

Cellulose fibres have high tensile strength which means that each one is difficult to pull apart. Up to 40% of the wall of a plant cell is made of cellulose. The arrangement of cellulose fibres gives shape to the cell as it grows.

The mechanical strength of the fibres also means that plant cells can withstand the large hydrostatic pressures that develop inside them without bursting as the result of osmosis.

Questions

1. How do the structures of α glucose and β glucose molecules differ?

2. Briefly explain why plant cells do not burst when large hydrostatic pressures develop inside them as the result of osmosis.

3. Why do starch and glycogen have little effect on the osmotic properties of cells?

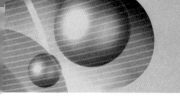

2.09 Plant and animal cells

OBJECTIVES

By the end of the section you should

○ know the structure of a leaf palisade cell as seen with an optical microscope

○ be able to explain the adaptations of different plant cells

○ know the appearance, ultrastructure, and function of the cell wall and chloroplasts of a leaf palisade cell

○ know the differences between plants cells and animal cells

Before you start, it will help to read sections **1.08** (microscopes), **1.11** (osmosis), and **2.08** (cellulose).

Some structures are found in all cells. Others are found only in some cells. Comparing a human cheek cell with a palisade cell from a leaf illustrates the similarities and differences.

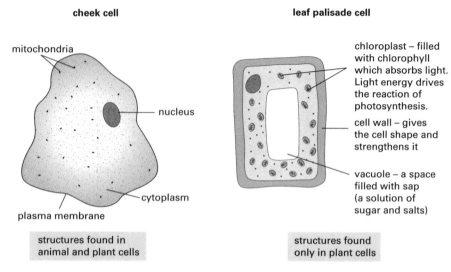

The structure of a human cheek cell and a leaf palisade cell seen with an optical microscope

Adaptations of plant cells

Different types of cell form the tissues of a plant. The adaptations of each type enable the tissues to carry out particular functions. What each type of cell looks like often helps us to understand what its function is.

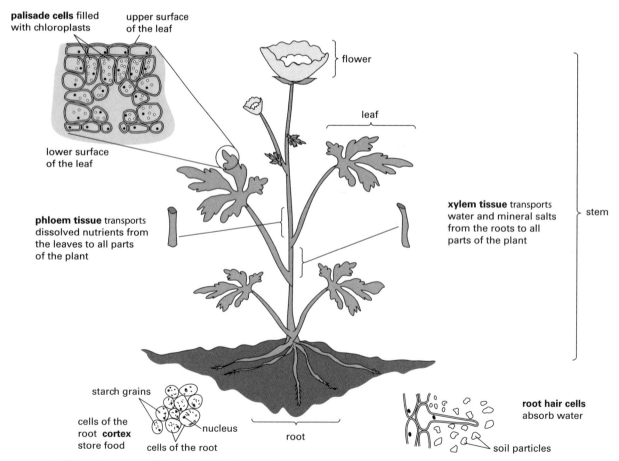

Different types of cell form the tissues of the plant body. There are fewer types than in the tissues of the human body.

- **Root hairs** fringe the tips of roots. Their finger-like extensions increase the surface area of roots, maximizing their absorption of water from the soil.
- **Xylem tissue** consists of tube-like cells which run from the tips of the root through the stem and out into every leaf and flower. It carries water and salts in solution to all parts of the plant. Spiral structures running round the walls of the tubes of the xylem are made of a substance called **lignin** which strengthens and waterproofs the walls of each tube. Strengthening helps xylem to support the plant and keep it upright.
- **Phloem tissue** consists of **companion** cells and **sieve** cells, which are also tube-like. The sieve tubes of phloem run by the side of the tubes of xylem. Sieve tubes transport dissolved nutrients and other substances in solution to all parts of the plant.
- **Cortex tissue** consists of large cells which form the bulk of root tissue. In plants like carrots large amounts of starch are stored in the cells of the root cortex.

Plant cell ultrastructure

Cell wall structure and function

The cell wall enables plant cells to withstand the large pressures that develop inside them as a result of osmosis. The structure of the cell wall makes this possible.

- Up to 40% of the wall of a plant cell is made of fibres of cellulose.
- Sieve fibres have high tensile strength which means that each one is difficult to pull apart.
- The criss-cross framework of fibres adds strength to the cell wall.

Chloroplast structure and function

The chloroplasts of plant cells harness light energy, enabling the plant to produce food by photosynthesis.

- Inside a chloroplast, membranes (**thylakoids**) are folded into stacks (**grana**).
- The thylakoids are sac-like and enclose molecules of chlorophyll and other light absorbing pigments. Their folding increases their surface area.
  - As a result the amount of light absorbed by chlorophyll and other pigments is maximized.
- Tubular extensions join together adjacent grana. The grana and their extensions are embedded in a gelatinous **stroma**.
- The reactions of photosynthesis take place in the chloroplasts. The products are stored as starch grains in the stroma.

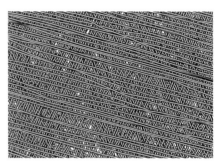

The framework of cellulose fibres forming the plant cell wall

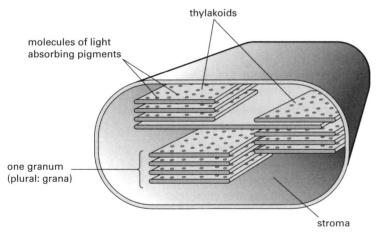

The structure of a chloroplast

labels: thylakoids; molecules of light absorbing pigments; one granum (plural: grana); stroma

Questions

1 Explain the relationship between the structure and function of a chloroplast.
2 Summarize the similarities and differences between plant cells and animal cells.
3 Explain the role of lignin in xylem tissue.

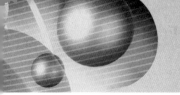

2.10 DNA replication

OBJECTIVES

By the end of the section you should understand

○ *that during the replication of DNA*

- *the hydrogen bonds linking the complementary bases of polynucleotide strands break*

- *DNA nucleotides are attracted to and bond with the exposed complementary bases*

- *different enzymes catalyse the breaking and bonding reactions*

Before you start, it will help to read sections **2.02** (DNA structure) and **2.11** (cell cycle).

Fact file

The replication of DNA is a very accurate process. Errors of copying (gene mutations) occur about once for every billion (1×10^9) nucleotides linked to template DNA. It seems that DNA polymerase 'proof reads' its own activity of linking nucleotides and cuts out any linkage 'mistakes' from the growing strand of new DNA.

Questions

1 What are the roles of DNA helicase and DNA polymerase during DNA replication?

2 Why is DNA replication described as semi-conservative?

3 What does the phrase 'DNA template strand' mean?

Making an exact copy

During **replication** DNA makes an exact copy of itself. The process is a necessary part of the division of a cell nucleus.

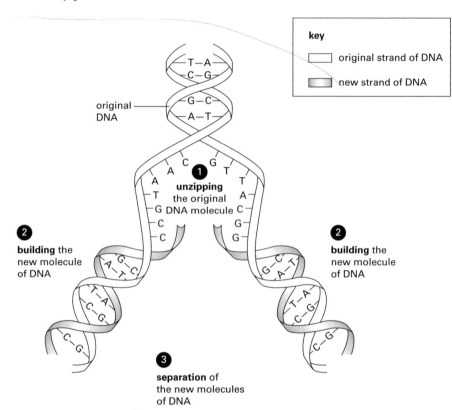

DNA replication – each strand of unzipped DNA is a pattern (template) against which a new strand forms.

There are three stages.

❶ Unzipping the original DNA molecule:
- The enzyme **DNA helicase** catalyses the breaking of hydrogen bonds linking the base pairs of the two strands of DNA.
- The double helix unzips as the base pairs separate.

❷ Building the new polynucleotide chain of DNA:
- Nucleotides free in solution within the nucleus each link with their complementary base on either of the unzipped strands of DNA (each called a template strand). Linkage is catalysed by the enzyme **DNA polymerase**.
- The process repeats itself again and again in the 5′ → 3′ → 5′ direction along both strands of template DNA.
- ⓡ As a result a new polynucleotide strand grows against each template strand.

❸ Separation of the new DNA molecules:
- When all of the bases of each template strand of DNA are each joined with the complementary base of a free nucleotide and these nucleotides have linked together, replication is complete.
- The two new molecules of DNA separate.

Semi-conservative replication

DNA replication occurs during interphase. The process is **semi-conservative** in that each new DNA molecule consists of a strand of template DNA (arising from the unzipping of the original double helix) and a strand of DNA formed as a complement of the template strand.

2.11 The cell cycle, mitosis, and cancer

OBJECTIVES

By the end of the section you should

○ *be able to identify the stages of the cell cycle*

○ *be able to name and explain the events occurring during each stage of mitosis*

○ *understand that damage to the genes which control the cell cycle may result in cancer*

Before you start, it will help to read sections **1.19** (monoclonal antibodies) and **2.05** (meiosis).

The cell cycle

New cells are formed from existing cells.
- The cells that give rise to new cells are called **parent** cells.
- The new cells are the **daughter** cells formed when the parent cell divides.

The **cell cycle** describes the process.

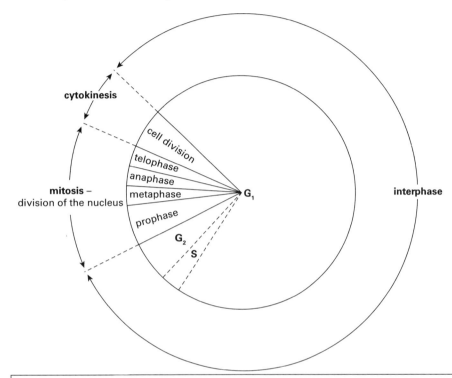

key		
G₁ – the cell grows and most of its organelles are replicated	**S** – replication of DNA. Each length of DNA forms a pair of strands. The strands of a pair are identical, each forming a **chromatid** which is the **sister** of its partner. Sister chromatids are joined at the **centromere**.	**G₂** – replication of the centrioles

The cell cycle of an animal cell takes between 8–24 hours to complete.

Interphase

The genetic material in the cell's nucleus appears under the optical microscope as diffuse **chromatin**. The different phases of interphase are called **G₁**, **S**, and **G₂**.

Mitosis

Mitosis follows interphase. The replicated DNA (in the form of chromatids) of the parent cell appears as distinct chromosomes under the optical microscope.

The diagram of mitosis (on the next page) in an animal cell illustrates just four chromosomes as paired chromatids.
- The movements of the chromatids during mitosis in a plant cell are identical, except that spindle formation takes place in the *absence* of centrioles.
- Remember that a cell inherits **two** sets of chromosomes, which is why the parent cell and its daughter cells are said to be diploid – one set from the **male parent**, the other set from the **female parent**. The symbol 2*n* represents the diploid state where *n* = the number in a set of chromosomes (2*n* = 4 in the parent cell and daughter cells of the diagram).
- Mitosis increases cell numbers in an organism. The growth and repair of tissues depends on mitosis.

Fact file

Colchicine is a chemical extracted from crocus corms. Metaphase can be seen more clearly if colchicine is added to a culture of cells undergoing mitosis. Spindle formation is inhibited preventing the separation of chromatids during anaphase.

Feulgen's solution stains DNA dark purple. Staining mitotic cells with Feulgen's solution makes it easier to visualize their chromosomes through the optical microscope.

Cytokinesis

Cytokinesis follows division of the nucleus at the end of telophase. Organelles such as mitochondria and chloroplasts are evenly distributed between the poles of the parent cells as its cytoplasm divides.

- In animal cells filaments of the protein **actin** attach to the inner surface of the plasma membrane in the region of the equator of the parent cells. The filaments contract, pulling the plasma membrane inwards. A 'waist' or **division furrow** forms which deepens, eventually splitting the parent cell into two daughter cells.
- In plant cells the Golgi apparatus forms vesicles containing carbohydrates (e.g. cellulose) in the middle of the parent cell. The vesicles fuse forming a **cell plate** which extends outwards until it meets the plasma membrane. A new cell wall forms, splitting the parent cell into two daughter cells.

What causes cancer?

Various factors in the environment may affect the cell cycle. If the genes that control cell division mutate and cell division runs out of control, then a cancer may develop. The mutated gene that leads to a cancer is called an **oncogene**. There are more than 200 different types of cancer.

A factor that causes gene mutation is called a **mutagen**. If the effect of a mutagen results in an oncogene, and therefore the development of a cancer, it is called a **carcinogen**. The majority of mutagens are carcinogens.

Chemicals

Many of the chemicals in the tar of tobacco smoke are carcinogens.

- Tobacco carcinogens cause the mutation of **tumour suppressor** genes which normally *inhibit* cell division. They may cause their loss or inactivation.
  - As a result cell division runs out of control, leading to the development of lung cancer.
- The tumour suppressor gene called *p53* is most frequently involved.

Tobacco carcinogens also affect the genes that *stimulate* cell division.

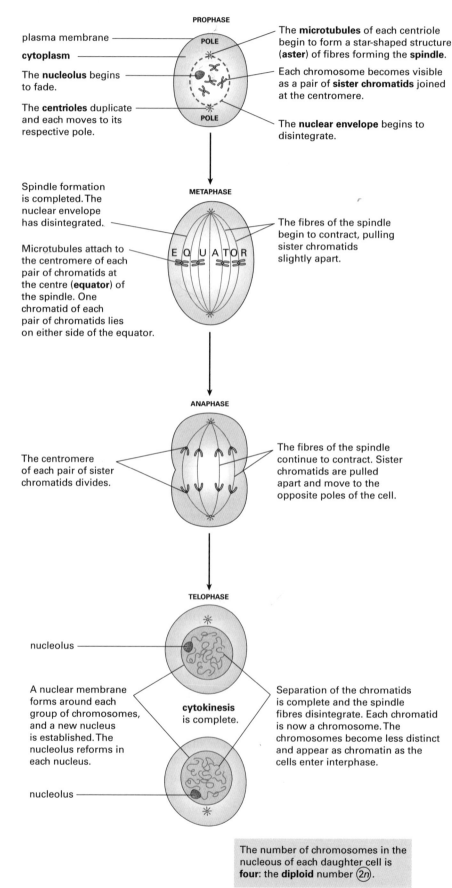

The **diploid** number (2n) of chromosomes of the parent cell is **four.**

PROPHASE

plasma membrane

cytoplasm

The **nucleolus** begins to fade.

The **centrioles** duplicate and each moves to its respective pole.

POLE

POLE

The **microtubules** of each centriole begin to form a star-shaped structure (**aster**) of fibres forming the **spindle.**

Each chromosome becomes visible as a pair of **sister chromatids** joined at the centromere.

The **nuclear envelope** begins to disintegrate.

METAPHASE

Spindle formation is completed. The nuclear envelope has disintegrated.

Microtubules attach to the centromere of each pair of chromatids at the centre (**equator**) of the spindle. One chromatid of each pair of chromatids lies on either side of the equator.

E Q U A T O R

The fibres of the spindle begin to contract, pulling sister chromatids slightly apart.

ANAPHASE

The centromere of each pair of sister chromatids divides.

The fibres of the spindle continue to contract. Sister chromatids are pulled apart and move to the opposite poles of the cell.

TELOPHASE

nucleolus

A nuclear membrane forms around each group of chromosomes, and a new nucleus is established. The nucleolus reforms in each nucleus.

nucleolus

cytokinesis is complete.

Separation of the chromatids is complete and the spindle fibres disintegrate. Each chromatid is now a chromosome. The chromosomes become less distinct and appear as chromatin as the cells enter interphase.

The number of chromosomes in the nucleous of each daughter cell is **four:** the **diploid** number (2n).

Mitosis in an animal cell. The stages of mitosis are **prophase**, **metaphase**, **anaphase**, and **telophase**. The memory aid **ProMAT** will help you to remember the sequence.

- Normally the genes 'switch off' when their task is done. If the tobacco carcinogens convert the genes to oncogenes which do not 'switch off' then cells proliferate and cancers develop.
- The *ras* oncogenes are the oncogenes most commonly involved (25% of lung cancer).

Ionizing radiation

Ionizing radiations include γ (gamma)-rays, X-rays and particles from the decay of radioactive elements. They damage DNA by **ionization** (stripping electrons from its molecules). The damage may lead to the development of a cancer.

Treating cancer

If detected at an early stage of development, many cancers can be cured by

- **surgery** – the cancer is removed
- **chemotherapy** – drugs which block one or more stages of the cell cycle
- **radiotherapy** – the cancer is bombarded and destroyed by a stream of particles emitted by a radioactive source.

However, left untreated, cancerous cells can break away from the original (**primary**) tumour, spread (a process called **metastasis**) and set up **secondary** growths elsewhere in the body, endangering the person's life.

Discovering new treatments for cancer is a very active area of scientific research.

- **Vaccines** have been developed against cancer-causing viruses.
- **Gene therapy** aims to replace the faulty genes which cause cancer with healthy genes.
- **Monoclonal antibodies** target cancer cells. When combined with an anti-cancer drug, the monoclonal antibodies deliver the drug to the cancer cells without affecting healthy cells.

Early detection before the cancer can spread in the body remains the basis of successful treatment.

Questions

1 The diagram illustrates the change in DNA content during the cell cycle.

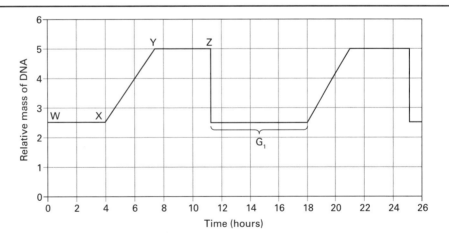

  a Calculate the percentage of the cell cycle time spent in G_1.

  b At which point does chromosome replication begin? Explain your answer.

  c At which point does cytokinesis begin? Explain your answer.

  d At which point does mitosis begin? Explain your answer.

2 What is an oncogene?

3 Briefly summarize ways of treating cancer.

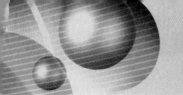

2.12 Cell differentiation and adaptation

OBJECTIVES

By the end of the section you should

○ *know that the undifferentiated cells of an early embryo develop into specialized types of cell which form the tissues of the individual*

○ *understand that the cells of multicellular organisms are organized into tissues, tissues into organs, and organs into organ systems*

Before you start, it will help to read sections **1.03** (digestive system), **1.08** (microscopes), and **1.14** (trachea and alveoli).

Differentiation

The cells of an embryo at an early stage all look alike. They are **undifferentiated**. As the embryo develops, it forms different tissues for different functions. Each cell in an early embryo has the capacity to develop into any of the types of cells needed to make up these tissues. The cells are called **embryonic stem cells**.

- The term **differentiation** refers to the process which enables undifferentiated cells to develop into particular types of cell.
- Following differentiation, the cells are said to be **differentiated**.

Differentiated cells are **specialized**, enabling them to carry out particular functions – for example producing mucus and conducting nerve impulses.

- Specialization adapts cells, enabling them to carry out different tasks.

Differentiation is an exact sequence of events during embryonic development. It lays down the features of the embryo in the right place at the right time.

- The process is controlled by **developmental genes**.
- These genes switch their activity 'on' and 'off' in the correct order to ensure the proper development of an embryo.

Tissues

A tissue is a group of cells of the same type. Different types of tissue include connective, muscle, nerve, and epithelial tissue.

Epithelia are tissues which cover the inside and outside of body surfaces. Each type has a particular function:

- **Protection** of internal organs from damage – for example, skin cells are thickened with the protein keratin which helps the cells to resist abrasion.
- **Diffusion** of substances across the surface of the epithelium – for example, the wall of the alveolus is a simple flattened epithelium one cell thick. Oxygen and carbon dioxide easily diffuse across its surface.

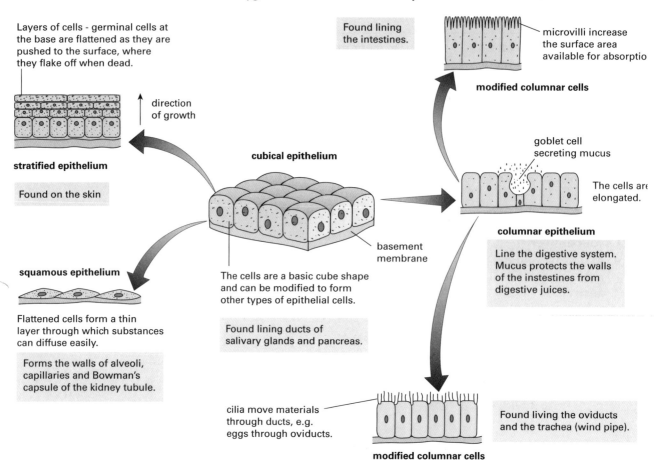

The variety of epithelial cells

- **Absorption** of materials – for example, the free surface of the cells covering the villi of the small intestine are folded into microvilli. The increase in surface area maximizes the rate of absorption of digested food.
- **Secretion** of substances onto the surface of the epithelium – for example, **goblet cells** secrete mucus onto the surface of the epithelium lining the tubes of the trachea and bronchi through which air passes to and from the lungs.

The appearance of epithelial cells seen with the optical microscope is often a clue to their function.

Organs and organ systems

Different tissues working together make up an **organ**. Different organs combine to make an **organ system**.

- The skin is the largest organ in the human body. Other organs include the liver, kidney, heart, stomach, lungs, brain, ovary and many more.
- Organ systems in the human body include the lymphatic, respiratory, digestive, urinary, reproductive, muscular, skeletal, nervous, endocrine, integumentary (skin, hair, etc.) and circulatory systems.

Plants also have tissues, organs and organ systems. The diagram shows their arrangement in a leaf.

<table>
<tr><td>

Questions

1 Briefly explain the role of genes in the development of the embryo.

2 Why is the appearance of epithelial cells often a clue to their function?

3 Briefly explain the difference between a tissue, organ, and organ system.

</td></tr>
</table>

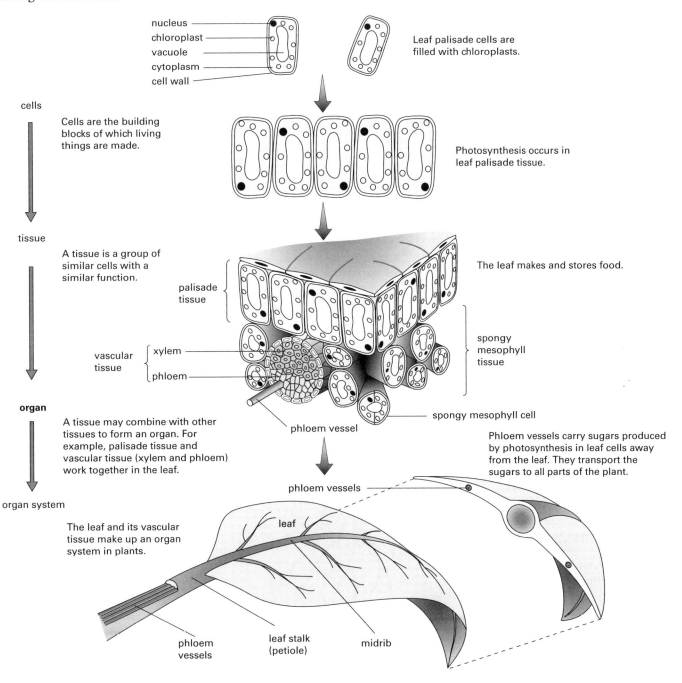

nucleus
chloroplast
vacuole
cytoplasm
cell wall

Leaf palisade cells are filled with chloroplasts.

cells

Cells are the building blocks of which living things are made.

Photosynthesis occurs in leaf palisade tissue.

tissue

A tissue is a group of similar cells with a similar function.

palisade tissue

The leaf makes and stores food.

vascular tissue — xylem / phloem

spongy mesophyll tissue

spongy mesophyll cell

organ

A tissue may combine with other tissues to form an organ. For example, palisade tissue and vascular tissue (xylem and phloem) work together in the leaf.

phloem vessel

Phloem vessels carry sugars produced by photosynthesis in leaf cells away from the leaf. They transport the sugars to all parts of the plant.

organ system

The leaf and its vascular tissue make up an organ system in plants.

phloem vessels

leaf

phloem vessels

leaf stalk (petiole)

midrib

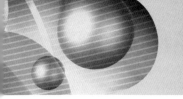

OBJECTIVES

By the end of the section you should

○ *understand the importance of surface area to volume ratios to living organisms*

Before you start, it will help to read sections **1.12** (surface area), **1.14** (alveoli), **2.14** (diffusion), and **2.15** (lamellae).

Notice:

- The SA/V of cube B is half that of cube A.
- The SA/V of cube C is two-thirds that of cube B and one-third that of cube A.

Remember:

- The *larger* the cube becomes, the *smaller* its SA/V because SA increases more slowly than V.
- Surface area increases with the **square** (power^2) of the side.
- Volume increase with the **cube** (power^3) of the side.

Qs and As

Q Why does a small mammal such as a vole (a rodent about 5 cm long) eat its own weight of food each day?

A *A vole's body has a large surface area relative to its volume. Much heat therefore is lost from its body through the skin to the environment. So, it needs lots of food as a source of energy to help maintain a constant body temperature.*

Questions

1 Explain why the surface area to volume ratio (SA/V) of large organisms is less than that of small organisms.

2 Briefly explain why an increase in size might be a stimulus for a cell to divide.

Exchanging materials across a surface

All cells (tissues, organs, organisms) exchange gases, food and other materials with their environment. These exchanges occur across the surfaces of epithelia. The larger the surface, the more material can be exchanged.

Surface area to volume ratio

The diagram and table show calculations of surface area (SA) and volume (V) for three cubes of different sizes. (Remember that a cube has six faces.)

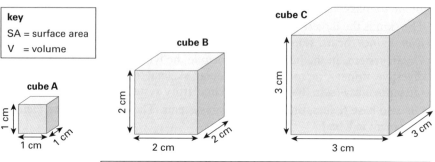

key
SA = surface area
V = volume

	cube A	cube B	cube C
SA of one face	$1 \times 1 = 1$ cm^2	$2 \times 2 = 4$ cm^2	$3 \times 3 = 9$ cm^2
SA of cube	1cm$^2 \times 6 = 6$ cm^2	4 cm$^2 \times 6 = 24$ cm^2	9 cm$^2 \times 6 = 54$ cm^2
V of cube	$1 \times 1 \times 1 = 1$ cm^3	$2 \times 2 \times 2 = 8$ cm^3	$3 \times 3 \times 3 = 27$ cm^3
$\dfrac{SA}{V}$	$\dfrac{6}{1} = 6$	$\dfrac{24}{8} = 3$	$\dfrac{54}{27} = 2$

Cells (tissues, organs, organisms) are not usually cubical, but the calculations apply to any shape. For example, as a cell grows it

- takes in more nutrients and gases
- produces more waste substances

After the cell reaches a certain size, its surface area becomes too small to take in enough of the substances it needs and remove enough of the wastes it produces. At this point the cell divides into two smaller daughter cells whose surface area to volume ratio is greater than that of the parent cell, enabling enough

- food and gases to pass into the cells
- wastes to pass out of the cells

Organ systems specialized for exchanging materials

All organisms exchange gases, food, and other materials between themselves and the environment. The exchanges take place across body surfaces.

Different adaptations increase surface area, maximizing the exchange of materials between an organism and its surroundings.

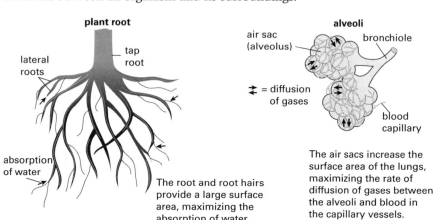

The root and root hairs provide a large surface area, maximizing the absorption of water.

The air sacs increase the surface area of the lungs, maximizing the rate of diffusion of gases between the alveoli and blood in the capillary vessels.

Adaptations of these organs increase their surface area to volume ratios.

2.14 Gas exchange 1

OBJECTIVES

By the end of the section you should

○ *be able to explain the adaptations of gas exchange surfaces*

○ *know how gas exchange occurs across (a) the surface of a single celled organism and (b) the leaves of dicotyledonous plants*

Before you start, it will help to read sections **1.11** (diffusion) and **2.17** (transpiration).

Diffusion across membranes

All organisms exchange oxygen and carbon dioxide between themselves and their environment. The gases are exchanged by diffusion across surface membranes. The membranes have properties that help to maximize the rate of diffusion. They

- are thin – the thinner the membrane, the more quickly gas molecules pass through it
- have a large surface area – the larger the surface area of a membrane, the more molecules of gas collide with it and pass through
- are permeable to the gases
- are moist – gases are exchanged in solution

Also, the rate of diffusion of gases across a membrane increases the steeper their respective concentration gradients are on either side of the membrane.

Why do organisms exchange oxygen and carbon dioxide with the environment?

The chemical reactions of **cellular respiration** release energy which powers the activities of organisms.

- The reactions of **aerobic respiration** (a form of cellular respiration) require oxygen.
  - As a result air containing oxygen passes into organisms which live on land, or oxygen in solution passes into organisms which live in water.
- Carbon dioxide is a waste product of aerobic respiration.
  - As a result carbon dioxide passes to the air or water from organisms.
- In plants the reactions of photosynthesis produce oxygen.
- If the rate of photosynthesis is greater than that of aerobic respiration (for example in bright light) then more oxygen will be produced than the plant requires for aerobic respiration.
  - As a result oxygen passes from the plant to the environment.
- If the rate of photosynthesis is less than that of respiration (for example in dim light) then less oxygen will be produced than the plant requires for aerobic respiration.
  - As a result oxygen passes to the plant from the environment.

Gas exchange in *Amoeba*

Amoeba proteus is a single-celled organism about 0.5 mm in diameter. It lives in freshwater. Its small size means that its surface area is large relative to its volume.

The cell's surface membrane is bathed in water containing dissolved oxygen.

- The concentration of dissolved oxygen outside the cell is greater than the concentration of oxygen inside the cell.
  - As a result oxygen diffuses down its concentration gradient from the water into the cell.
- The rate of diffusion of oxygen across the membrane is sufficient to satisfy the oxygen requirements of the cell.

Carbon dioxide is produced by aerobic respiration inside the cell.

- The concentration of carbon dioxide inside the cell is greater than the concentration of carbon dioxide in solution outside.
  - As a result carbon dioxide diffuses down its concentration gradient from the cell into the water.

Oxygen uptake and consumption by the cell and its carbon dioxide production and output are continuous processes which take place at the same time.

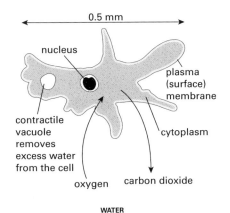

Gas exchange in *Amoeba proteus*

Fact file

The **cotyledon** is the part of a seed in which starch is stored. The starch is a source of energy during germination, when the embryo plant grows and develops.

Seeds with two cotyledons are called **dicotyledonous** seeds. The leaves of plants whose seeds are dicotyledonous are broad – the so-called broad-leaved plants.

Fact file

Any characteristic which increases an organism's chances of surviving in its habitat is called an **adaptation**. The term **xerophytic** refers to plants able to survive in hot, dry conditions.

Cacti are xerophytic plants. The adaptations of cacti are a compromise between the opposing requirements of gas exchange and the limitation of the loss of water from the plant to the environment.

Leaves are pointed **spines**, reducing their surface area and so reducing water loss. They also discourage animals from eating the cactus.

A thick **waxy waterproof layer** covering the surfaces reduces water loss.

Storage of water in the **thick stem** enables the cactus to survive long periods without rain.

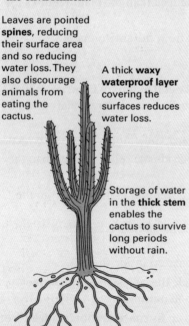

Long roots branch out just under the sand's surface. The **large surface area** of the roots enables the cactus to **maximize absorption** of what little water is available.

Gas exchange across the leaves of plants

The diagram shows how different adaptations maximize the exchange of gases between the leaves of a plant and the environment.

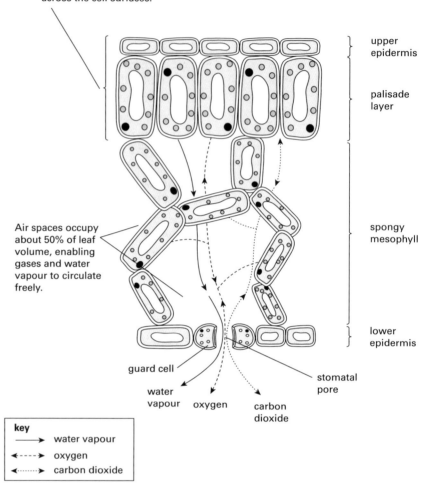

The surfaces of the cells of the palisade and spongy mesophyll tissues are gas exchange surfaces in the leaf. They are moist and permeable. Gases in solution are quickly exchanged across the cell surfaces.

Air spaces occupy about 50% of leaf volume, enabling gases and water vapour to circulate freely.

upper epidermis

palisade layer

spongy mesophyll

lower epidermis

guard cell

water vapour   oxygen   carbon dioxide

stomatal pore

key
→ water vapour
◄---► oxygen
◄······► carbon dioxide

The gas exchange surfaces inside the leaf of a dicotyledonous plant

Notice that the under surface of the leaf is perforated with gaps called stomata. Each **stoma** (singular) is flanked by **guard cells** which contain chloroplasts.

- Recall that the direction of the net movement of oxygen and carbon dioxide molecules between the inside of a leaf and the atmosphere depends on the balance between the rate of photosynthesis and the rate of aerobic respiration of the leaf's tissues.
- When the concentration of carbon dioxide produced in aerobic respiration balances that used in photosynthesis, then the net exchange of carbon dioxide between the leaf and the atmosphere is zero. This is the **compensation point**.

Recall also that

- the spaces inside a leaf are saturated with water vapour
- the concentration of water vapour in the atmosphere is usually less than inside the leaf.

  ◉ As a result water vapour passes down its concentration gradient from inside the leaf, through the stomata perforating the under surface of the leaf to the atmosphere. The process is called **transpiration**.

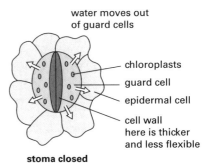

How stomata open and close

- When guard cells fill with water and become more turgid, their volume increases.
  - Ⓔ As a result the guard cells push each other apart and the pore opens.
- Guard cells become more turgid because of the active transport of potassium ions (K^+) into the cells from the surrounding cells of the leaf's lower epidermis. Active transport removes chloride ions (Cl^-) from the guard cells at the same time.
  - Ⓔ As a result of the exchange of ions, the water potential of the guard cells becomes more negative compared with the cells surrounding them.
  - Ⓔ As a result water passes into the guard cells from the surrounding cells by osmosis.
  - Ⓔ As a result the guard cells become turgid and bow outwards, opening the pore.
- The active transport of potassium ions and chloride ions is triggered by light and photosynthesis. Recall that the guard cells have chloroplasts; other cells of the leaf epidermis do not.
- In the dark (and absence of photosynthesis) the active transport of ions stops.
  - Ⓔ As a result the ions diffuse down their respective concentration gradients until equilibrium with the surrounding epidermal cells is reached.
  - Ⓔ As a result the water potential of the guard cells becomes less negative compared with the cells surrounding them.
  - Ⓔ As a result water passes from the guard cells into the surrounding cells by osmosis.
  - Ⓔ As a result the guard cells become less turgid and the pore closes.

water moves out of guard cells

chloroplasts
guard cell
epidermal cell
cell wall here is thicker and less flexible

stoma closed

water moves into guard cells

chloroplasts
stomatal pore
As turgid guard cells swell, the cell walls stretch unevenly, so the cells bow outwards and the pore opens.

stoma open

How stomata open and close

How science works (D)

Measuring oxygen consumption using a respirometer

The rate of oxygen consumption by living tissue can be measured using a **respirometer**. The diagram illustrates the apparatus.

The living pea seeds are germinating but not photosynthesizing. In other words they are exchanging oxygen and carbon dioxide with the environment as a result of respiration but not photosynthesis.

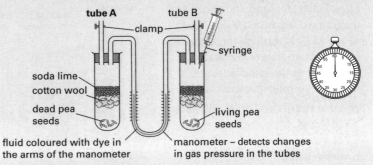

tube A   tube B
clamp
syringe
soda lime
cotton wool
dead pea seeds
living pea seeds
fluid coloured with dye in the arms of the manometer
manometer – detects changes in gas pressure in the tubes

The mass of the seeds is the same in tubes **A** and **B**.

- At the beginning of the experiment the clamp on tube **B** is closed and the clock started.
- The living seeds use the oxygen in tube **B** to oxidize sugar.
- The carbon dioxide produced is absorbed by the soda lime. So the pressure of gas in tube **B** decreases below that of the atmosphere.
  - Ⓔ As a result the fluid in the right hand arm of the manometer rises.
- After a set time the clock is stopped and the plunger of the syringe pushed in until the level of the fluid is the same in each arm of the manometer.
- The distance the plunger of the syringe is moved represents the volume of oxygen used by the mass of seeds in the set time (the volume of oxygen is written as $cm^3\ g^{-1}\ min^{-1}$).
- The value represents the **rate of respiration** of the germinating seeds.

Tube **A** contains the same mass dead pea seeds as there are living pea seeds in tube **B**. It is a barometer, correcting any changes in temperature and pressure in the apparatus. The clamp is left open in tube **A**.

Questions

1 Summarize the adaptations of gas exchange surfaces which maximize the rate of diffusion across them.

2 Explain why concentration gradients of oxygen and carbon dioxide across the surface of the single-celled organism *Amoeba proteus* enable it to exchange the gases between itself and its environment.

3 Summarize the process which controls the opening and closing of the stomata of a leaf.

2.15 Gas exchange 2

OBJECTIVES

By the end of the section you should

○ *know how gas exchange occurs across (a) the gills of a fish, and (b) the tracheal system of an insect*

Before you start, it will help to read sections **1.11** (diffusion), and **2.14** (gas exchange).

The lamellae at work

- The concentration of oxygen in water is greater than in the blood passing to the gills.
  - ℝ As a result oxygen diffuses from the water into the blood.
- The concentration of carbon dioxide in the blood passing to the gills is greater than in the water.
  - ℝ As a result carbon dioxide diffuses from blood into the water.
- The concentration gradients of gases between blood and water are maximized because the direction of blood flow through the lamellae is opposite to that of the water flowing over the lamellae – the so-called **counter-current** effect.
  - ℝ As a result the rate of diffusion of gases down their respective concentration gradients is maximized.
  - ℝ As a result the rate of exchange of gases between blood and water is maximized.

Flow of water

The flow of water through the mouth and over the lamellae is called the **respiratory current**.

- The opening and shutting of the mouth and opercula are coordinated.
  - ℝ As a result there is a continuous flow of water over the lamellae.
- Muscles control the opening of the gut. Their contraction closes the opening.
  - ℝ As a result water does not enter the gut from the mouth.

Gas exchange across the gills of bony fish

The **gill slits** are a series of openings on either side of the head of a fish.

- Each gill slit is separated from its neighbour by a thin, vertical bar of bone called the **gill arch**.
- Rows of leaf-like tissue called **lamellae** project from either side of the gill arch, forming the gill.
- Oxygen and carbon dioxide are exchanged across the lamellae between the blood flowing through them and the water flowing over them.
- The operculum is a bony flap which covers the gill slits.

Each lamella is folded into **gill plates**, increasing the surface area across which gases are exchanged. Vessels supplying the lamellae with blood branch into a dense capillary network within each lamella.

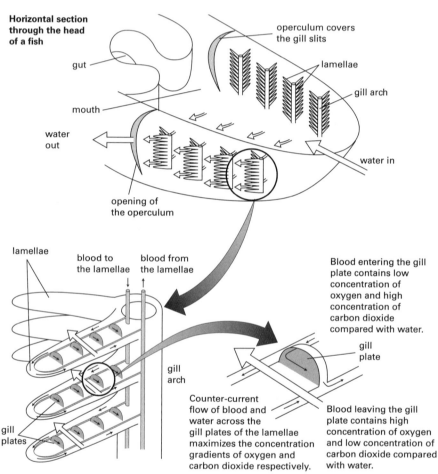

The gills of a fish are made up of gill arches, lamellae, and gill plates across which gas exchange takes place.

Inspiration – lowering the floor of the pharynx *increases* the volume of the mouth cavity and reduces pressure. Water flows in through the open mouth and over the lamellae.

Expiration – raising the floor of the pharynx *reduces* the volume of the mouth cavity and increases pressure. The **pressure pump** effect pushes water over the lamellae and against the opercula, pressing them open.

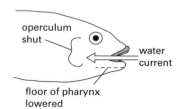

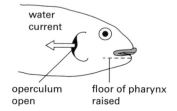

Gas exchange across the tracheae of insects

Most insects are **terrestrial** (live on land). Their bodies are covered by a hard outer **exoskeleton** which is impermeable to water. This helps prevent water loss from the insect's body (where there is a high concentration of water) to the atmosphere (where there is a relatively low concentration of water).

However, this waterproofing means that the exoskeleton is also impermeable to oxygen and carbon dioxide of the air. Air enters and leaves the insect body through a set of pores opening at the body's surface. The pores are connected to a system of tubes which branch to and throughout the body's tissues.

- The openings are called **spiracles**.
- The tubes are called **tracheae** and **tracheoles**. Tracheoles branch from the tracheae, are very fine and extend between the cells of the body's tissues.

Notice that the tracheae are supported by rings of chitin (a carbohydrate). The rings prevent collapse when the pressure of air inside the tracheae is less than atmospheric pressure.

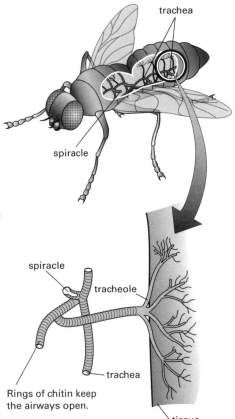

The tracheal system at work

❶ • A solution of gases and other substances fills the ends of tracheoles.
- Oxygen and carbon dioxide are exchanged between the solution filling the ends of tracheoles and the cells of tissues nearby. The gases diffuse down their respective concentration gradients.
- Oxygen is more concentrated in the solution filling the ends of the tracheoles than the cells of tissues nearby.
- Carbon dioxide is more concentrated in the cells of tissues nearby than in the solution filling the ends of the tracheoles.
  - 🄬 As a result oxygen is supplied to the tissues; carbon dioxide is removed from the tissues.

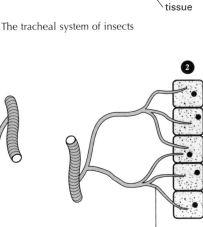

Rings of chitin keep the airways open.

The tracheal system of insects

❷ • At rest the water potential of the tissues is less negative than the solution in the tracheoles.
- If activity increases, respiration switches from aerobic to anaerobic.
  - 🄬 As a result lactic acid is produced in the cells of tissues.
  - 🄬 As a result the water potential of the tissues becomes more negative than the solution in the tracheoles.
  - 🄬 As a result water passes from the tracheoles to the tissues by osmosis.
  - 🄬 As a result of the loss of water, more air is drawn into the tracheoles.
  - 🄬 As a result more oxygen is available to tissues where the concentration of oxygen is low and more oxygen is therefore needed.

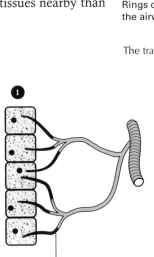
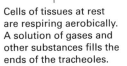

Cells of tissues at rest are respiring aerobically. A solution of gases and other substances fills the ends of the tracheoles.

Cells of tissues are active and respiring anaerobically. Air fills the ends of the tracheoles.

- When activity stops, the lactic acid is oxidized and the water potential in the tissues becomes less negative.
  - 🄬 As a result water passes from the tissues to the tracheoles by osmosis.
- In larger insects contraction and relaxation of the abdominal muscles **ventilates** the tracheal system.
  - 🄬 As a result the flow of air through the system increases.
- Fine hairs around the openings of the spiracles trap water vapour.
  - 🄬 As a result the concentration gradient of water between the insect's body and the atmosphere is reduced.
  - 🄬 As a result the loss of water from the insect's body is minimized.
- When conditions are particularly dry the spiracles may close altogether for a limited period.
  - 🄬 As a result the insect's body is sealed from the environment, preventing water loss.

Questions

1 Explain how gills are adapted so that the exchange of gases between water and the blood of a fish is maximized.

2 Explain how gas exchange takes place between the tracheae and tissues of an insect.

2.16 The blood system

OBJECTIVES

By the end of the section you should

○ be able to describe the circulatory system of a mammal

○ know the structure and function of arteries, veins, and capillary blood vessels

○ be able to explain exchanges between capillaries and tissues

○ understand the links between the lymphatic system and blood system

Before you start, it will help to read sections **1.11** (diffusion), **1.16** (heart), and **2.07** (oxygen transport).

Arteries are often described as carriers of blood enriched with oxygen (oxygenated blood) and veins as carriers of blood depleted of oxygen (deoxygenated blood).

The circulatory system

The heart pumps blood through tubular blood vessels (**arteries**, **veins**, and **capillaries**). Blood transports oxygen, digested food, hormones, and other substances to the tissues and organs of the body.

Chemical reactions taking place in cells produce carbon dioxide and other waste substances (e.g. urea). Blood transports the wastes from the tissues and organs of the body to where they are removed from the body.

Remember that:

• arteries carry blood from the heart
• veins carry blood to the heart
• capillaries link arteries and veins

The heart and blood vessels are the components of the circulatory system.

Notice in the diagram that

• the **pulmonary arteries** carry deoxygenated blood (to the lungs from the heart) and the pulmonary veins carry oxygenated blood (from the lungs to the heart)

• unlike other veins, the **hepatic portal vein** does not drain blood into the **vena cava** *en route* to the heart, but carries blood with its load of digested food from the intestine to the liver

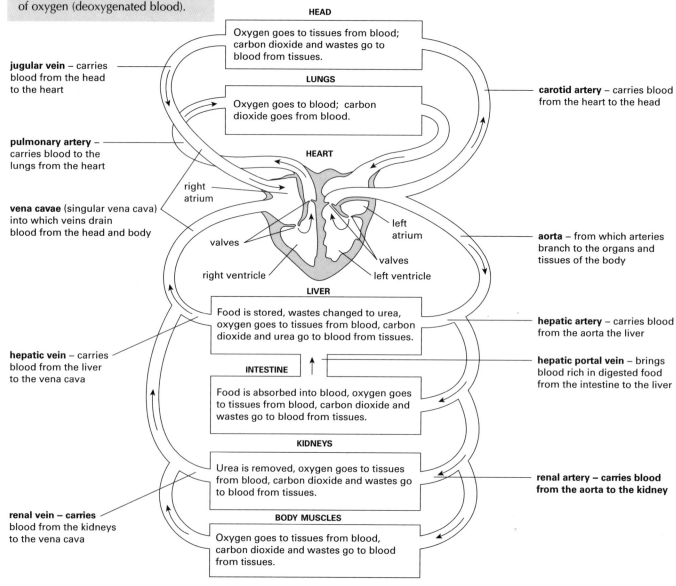

jugular vein – carries blood from the head to the heart

pulmonary artery – carries blood to the lungs from the heart

vena cavae (singular vena cava) into which veins drain blood from the head and body

hepatic vein – carries blood from the liver to the vena cava

renal vein – carries blood from the kidneys to the vena cava

carotid artery – carries blood from the heart to the head

aorta – from which arteries branch to the organs and tissues of the body

hepatic artery – carries blood from the aorta the liver

hepatic portal vein – brings blood rich in digested food from the intestine to the liver

renal artery – carries blood from the aorta to the kidney

HEAD
Oxygen goes to tissues from blood; carbon dioxide and wastes go to blood from tissues.

LUNGS
Oxygen goes to blood; carbon dioxide goes from blood.

HEART
right atrium
left atrium
valves
valves
right ventricle
left ventricle

LIVER
Food is stored, wastes changed to urea, oxygen goes to tissues from blood, carbon dioxide and urea go to blood from tissues.

INTESTINE
Food is absorbed into blood, oxygen goes to tissues from blood, carbon dioxide and wastes go to blood from tissues.

KIDNEYS
Urea is removed, oxygen goes to tissues from blood, carbon dioxide and wastes go to blood from tissues.

BODY MUSCLES
Oxygen goes to tissues from blood, carbon dioxide and wastes go to blood from tissues.

→ direction of blood flow

Blood vessels

The diagram compares the structure and functions of arteries and veins.

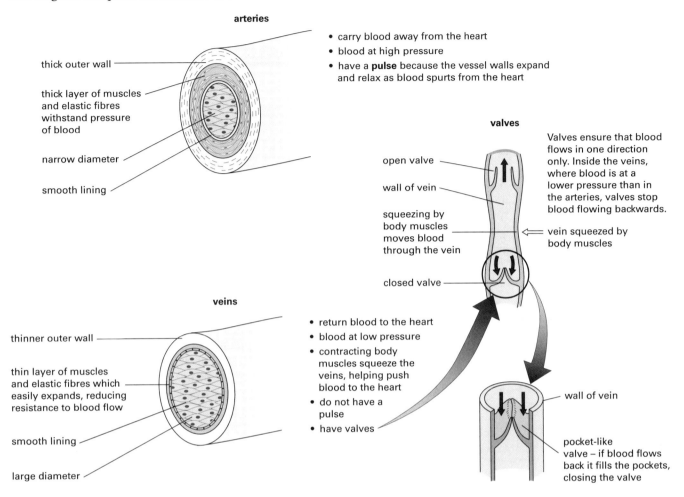

arteries

thick outer wall

thick layer of muscles and elastic fibres withstand pressure of blood

narrow diameter

smooth lining

- carry blood away from the heart
- blood at high pressure
- have a **pulse** because the vessel walls expand and relax as blood spurts from the heart

valves

open valve

wall of vein

squeezing by body muscles moves blood through the vein

closed valve

Valves ensure that blood flows in one direction only. Inside the veins, where blood is at a lower pressure than in the arteries, valves stop blood flowing backwards.

vein squeezed by body muscles

veins

thinner outer wall

thin layer of muscles and elastic fibres which easily expands, reducing resistance to blood flow

smooth lining

large diameter

- return blood to the heart
- blood at low pressure
- contracting body muscles squeeze the veins, helping push blood to the heart
- do not have a pulse
- have valves

wall of vein

pocket-like valve – if blood flows back it fills the pockets, closing the valve

Notice in the diagram:

- Blood in veins is at a lower pressure than blood in arteries.
- One-way valves inside the veins prevent blood from flowing backwards.
- The propulsive force of the heart beat keeps blood flowing away from the heart through the arteries, so there is no need for valves inside arteries.

Arteries and veins branch into smaller vessels.

- Arteries branch into **arterioles**.
- Veins branch into **venules**.
- Arterioles and venules branch further into microscopic **capillaries**.

Exchanges between capillaries and tissues, and the role of lymph

Remember:

- The walls of capillary blood vessels are one cell thick.
  - Ⓡ As a result substances easily diffuse between blood in the capillaries and the surrounding tissues
- The capillaries form dense networks called **capillary beds** in the tissues of the body, providing a *large surface area* which maximizes the rate of exchange of materials between the blood and tissues.
- The blood in capillaries supplies nearby cells with oxygen, food molecules, and other substances. It also carries away carbon dioxide and other waste produced by the cells' metabolism.

Refer to the diagrams on the next page as you read about the exchanges of substances between capillaries and tissues, and the movement of fluid into the lymphatic system.

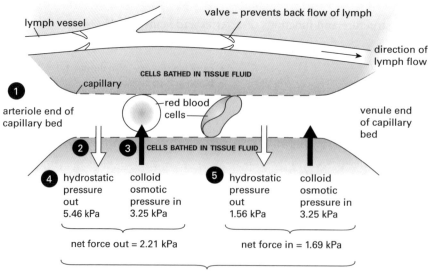

Exchanges between capillaries and tissues, and their relationship with the lymphatic system

6 overall force out = 2.21 – 1.69 = 0.52 kPa ... resulting in an excess of tissue fluid which drains into the lymph vessels

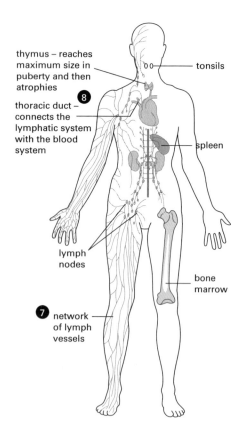

The network of lymph vessels is shown on the right-hand side of the body only. The tonsils, thymus, and spleen are part of the lymphatic system.

1 Hydrostatic pressure at the arteriole end of a capillary bed is high because of the force generated by contractions of the heart.

2 The pressure forces small molecules dissolved in the blood plasma through the walls of the capillaries into surrounding tissues. The plasma is now called **tissue fluid**.

3 Water escapes through the walls of the capillaries but not large protein molecules. So the water potential of the blood is lowered (more negative). This water potential is called the **colloid osmotic pressure** and has the effect of drawing molecules back into the blood capillaries.

4 At the arteriole end of a capillary bed, the hydrostatic pressure forcing molecules out of the capillary vessels is greater than that of the colloidal osmotic pressure drawing them in.

As a result there is a net outflow of substances in solution from the capillaries.

5 At the venule end of the capillary bed, the colloid osmotic pressure is greater than the hydrostatic pressure – which is now reduced because of the resistance of the capillary walls to the flow of blood through the capillary vessels.

As a result there is a net movement of substances in solution into the capillaries.

6 The movement of substances in solution out of the capillaries is greater than the return flow.

As a result an excess of fluid bathes the tissues.

7 The excess tissue fluid drains into the **lymph vessels** which pass to all of the tissues of the body, as the diagram shows. The tissue fluid is now called **lymph**.

8 The system of lymph vessels joins the blood system at the opening of the thoracic duct. Lymph continually circulates to the blood at this point.

As a result the volume of the lymph in the lymph vessels remains constant.

Questions

1 Identify some of the differences between arteries, veins, and capillary blood vessels.

2 Briefly describe the role of valves in veins.

3 Summarize the processes which lead to the exchange of substances between capillary blood vessels and tissues.

2.17 Water transport in plants

OBJECTIVES

By the end of the section you should

○ *know the structure of the root of a dicotyledonous plant*

○ *be able to describe the passage of water from the soil, through the plant to the atmosphere*

Before you start, it will help to read sections **1.11** (osmosis), **2.09** (plant cells), **2.11** (mitosis), **2.12** (differentiation), and **2.14** (leaves).

The structure of a dicotyledonous root

The root tip grows through the soil. Small, undifferentiated cells form a **region of growth** immediately behind the root cap. The cells repeatedly divide by mitosis.

Behind the region of growth is a **region of differentiation**. Here the cells become greatly enlarged as the vacuole of each cell forms.

- Cells of the epidermis (outer layer) differentiate into **root hair cells**, greatly increasing the surface area of the root, maximizing its absorption of water.
- Cells between the root hair cells and the central core of xylem and phloem differentiate into cells of the **cortex** and cells of the **endodermis** and **pericycle**.

The uptake and passage of water across the root

Root hairs are in intimate contact with soil particles. Water passes into the root by osmosis.

Some of the water takes the **apoplastic route**:

- Water passes into spaces between cellulose fibres within the cell walls of root hair cells.
- The water passes from root hair cells across the root from cell wall to cell wall.
- Its passage is due to the pull transmitted by the cohesive forces between water molecules as a result of hydrogen bonding.

Water also takes the **symplastic route** and **vacuolar route** across a root:

- Water passes from where its potential is high in the soil to where its potential is lower in the cells of the cortex.
- The difference in water potential (water potential gradient) between adjacent cells means that water moves by osmosis through the root hair cells and through the cells of the cortex to the xylem.

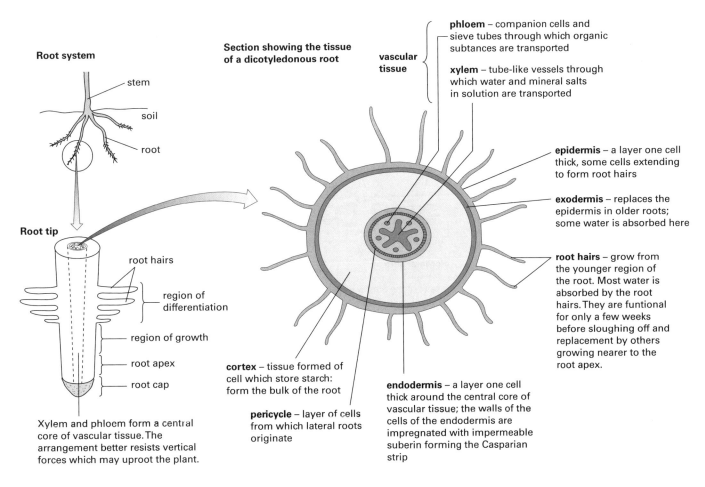

Root system

- stem
- soil
- root

Root tip

- root hairs
- region of differentiation
- region of growth
- root apex
- root cap

Xylem and phloem form a central core of vascular tissue. The arrangement better resists vertical forces which may uproot the plant.

Section showing the tissue of a dicotyledonous root

vascular tissue

phloem – companion cells and sieve tubes through which organic subtances are transported

xylem – tube-like vessels through which water and mineral salts in solution are transported

epidermis – a layer one cell thick, some cells extending to form root hairs

exodermis – replaces the epidermis in older roots; some water is absorbed here

root hairs – grow from the younger region of the root. Most water is absorbed by the root hairs. They are funtional for only a few weeks before sloughing off and replacement by others growing nearer to the root apex.

cortex – tissue formed of cell which store starch: form the bulk of the root

pericycle – layer of cells from which lateral roots originate

endodermis – a layer one cell thick around the central core of vascular tissue; the walls of the cells of the endodermis are impregnated with impermeable suberin forming the Casparian strip

- In the symplastic route water diffuses through the cytoplasm of *adjacent* cells.
- In the vacuolar route water diffuses through the *vacuoles* as well as the cytoplasm.

The impermeable **Casparian strip** seems to prevent the passage of water by the apoplastic route. Water therefore passes into the cytoplasm and vacuoles of the cells of the endodermis on its way to the xylem.

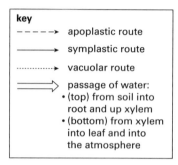

key
- – – – – → apoplastic route
- ───────→ symplastic route
- ·············→ vacuolar route
- ⟹ passage of water:
  - (top) from soil into root and up xylem
  - (bottom) from xylem into leaf and into the atmosphere

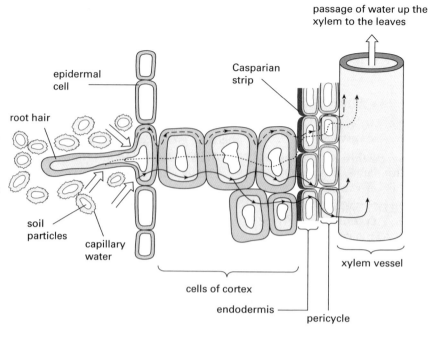

The passage of water across the leaf

The diagram shows the passage of water across the tissues of the leaf and the loss of water from the air spaces of the leaf to the atmosphere. Notice:

- Water moves from cell to cell by the apoplastic, symplastic, and vacuolar routes.
- The movement of water by the apoplastic route depends on the pull transmitted by the cohesive forces between water molecules. The apoplastic route accounts for most of the water moving between the cells of the leaf tissues.
- The movement of water by the symplastic and vacuolar routes depends on the difference in water potential (water potential gradient) between adjacent cells.
- The loss of water from the leaf depends on the difference in water potential (water potential gradient) between its air spaces and the atmosphere outside.

Overall there is a water potential gradient across the leaf from the leaf xylem to the atmosphere. The loss of water from the leaf through the stomata into the atmosphere is called **transpiration**.

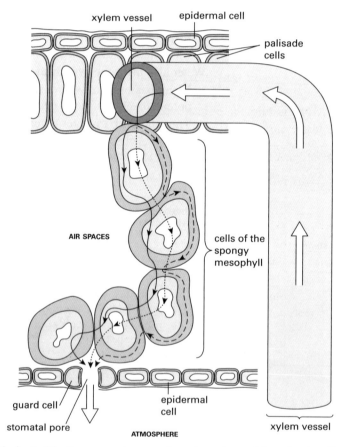

The heat of the Sun evaporates water from the surfaces of the palisade cells and spongy mesophyll cells. The water vapour saturates the air spaces of the leaf.

The movement of water up the xylem of the stem

As water is lost from the leaf through transpiration it is replaced by more water drawn by osmosis from the xylem of the leaf into the adjacent mesophyll cells.

The movement of water molecules into the tissues of the leaf pulls (draws up) other water molecules through the xylem of the stem. This is because of the pull of water molecules moving from wall-to-wall of the cells of the leaf's tissues by the apoplastic route. The effect is called **transpiration pull** and produces a state of tension in the columns of water within the xylem vessels.

Transpiration pull is possible because of the considerable cohesive forces between water molecules as a result of hydrogen bonding. These cohesive forces are sufficient to raise water to the tops of the tallest trees, and the theory of the mechanism is known as the **cohesion-tension theory**.

In summary

Water movement through the plant occurs because of

- the difference in water potential between the soil water and root tissue, and between leaf tissue and the atmosphere
- transpiration pull which produces tension in the columns of water within the xylem of the stem (made possible because of the cohesion of water molecules through hydrogen bonding)

Transpiration pull also reduces the hydrostatic pressure at the base of the xylem compared with the hydrostatic pressure which develops as water is drawn across the root. This difference in hydrostatic pressure is responsible for the entry of water into the xylem.

The forces generated as water is drawn across the root cause a build up of **root pressure**. This contributes to the movement of the water up the xylem of the stem, especially in the relatively short **herbaceous** (non-woody plants). However it does not account for the movement of water up tall trees.

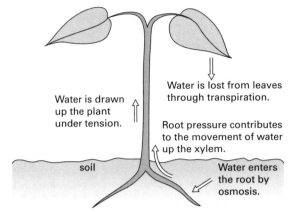

Water is lost from leaves through transpiration.

Water is drawn up the plant under tension.

Root pressure contributes to the movement of water up the xylem.

soil

Water enters the root by osmosis.

Movement of water in a whole plant

Rate of transpiration

The table below shows how different factors affect the rate of transpiration. These factors cause changes in the

- concentration gradient of water vapour between the inside of the leaf and the atmosphere outside (cause **A**)
- size of the aperture of the stomatal pores (cause **B**)
- kinetic motion of water molecules (cause **C**)

Factor	Rate of transpiration		Cause
	Increase	Decrease	
humidity	low	high	A – The steeper the concentration gradient, the faster is the rate of transpiration.
wind condition	windy	still	
light	bright	dim	B – The larger the aperture, the faster is the rate of transpiration.
temperature	high	low	C – An increase in temperature increases the kinetic motion of water molecules. The greater their kinetic motion, the greater is the rate of transpiration.

How science works (A)

Mass transport

Some substances are needed by organisms and obtained from the environment. Other substances are wastes produced by organisms and removed to the environment.

In very small organisms substances are exchanged by diffusion. In large organisms diffusion is too slow to meet their needs. Different systems of **mass transport** are needed to move substances rapidly from one part of a large organism to another.

The systems link with exchange surfaces where differences in concentration of substances and in pressure of gases propel substances

- from where they are exchanged

- to where they are needed by tissues or removed to the environment.

The blood system of mammals and the xylem and phloem tissues of plants are examples of mass transport systems.

Questions

1 Explain the roles of the endodermis and pericycle in the root of a dicotyledonous plant.

2 The terms 'apoplastic route' and 'symplastic route' refer to the passage of water across the roots and leaves of a dicotyledonous plant. Explain the difference between the two terms.

3 Summarize the processes by which water passes from the soil, into a plant, through the plant and into the atmosphere.

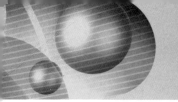

2.18 Classification and taxonomy

OBJECTIVES

By the end of the section you should

○ *know that most types of classification reflect phylogenetic relationships*

○ *know that organisms are classified into groups according to their shared characteristics*

○ *understand the difficulties of defining species*

○ *understand the principles of taxonomy*

Fact file

The Swedish scientist Carl von Linné (better known as Carolus Linnaeus) devised the binomial system for naming organisms. He also laid the foundations of the system of classification we use today.

Classification

Organisms which have characteristics in common are grouped together. Placing organisms into groups is called **classification**.

Some characteristics are unique to a group – there is no overlap with other groups. Other characteristics are shared with other groups. Groups therefore combine to form larger groups forming a hierarchy of groups (or **taxa**). The largest group of all is the **kingdom**.

Each

- kingdom includes a number of **phyla** (plural)
- phyl**um** (singular) includes a number of **classes**
- class includes a number of **orders**
- order includes a number of **families**
- family includes a number of **genera** (plural)
- gen**us** (singular) includes one or more **species**.

Taxonomy

The term **taxonomy** refers to the strict methods and rules of classification. For example the **genus** and the **species** identify the individual living thing. Humans belong to the genus *Homo* and have the species name *sapiens*; barn owls are called *Tyto alba*.

Since the name of each living thing is in two parts, the method of naming is called the **binomial system** ('bi' means 'two'). Notice that

- the genus name begins with a capital letter
- the species name begins with a small letter
- the whole name is printed in *italics*

Phylogeny

The more characteristics that organisms have in common, the closer is the relationship between the individuals. By 'relationship' we mean the characteristics individuals have as a result of a shared evolutionary history which links them to a common ancestor. The term **phylogeny** refers to the evolutionary history of organisms.

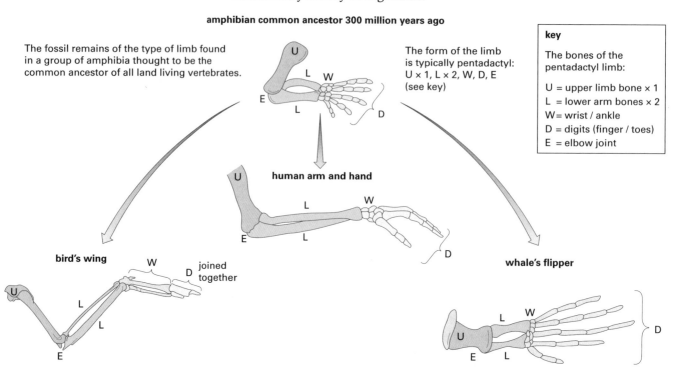

amphibian common ancestor 300 million years ago

The fossil remains of the type of limb found in a group of amphibia thought to be the common ancestor of all land living vertebrates.

The form of the limb is typically pentadactyl: U × 1, L × 2, W, D, E (see key)

key

The bones of the pentadactyl limb:

U = upper limb bone × 1
L = lower arm bones × 2
W = wrist / ankle
D = digits (finger / toes)
E = elbow joint

human arm and hand

bird's wing

joined together

whale's flipper

Different forms of the pentadactyl limb have evolved in descendants of the common ancestor of vertebrates over many millions of years.

Most types of classification reflect phylogenetic relationships. For example the group **vertebrates** includes the amphibia, reptiles, birds, and mammals. A backbone and pentadactyl limbs (five digits on each limb) are characteristics they have in common as the result of a shared phylogeny.

Investigating phylogenetic relationships between organisms helps us to understand the evolution of life on Earth.

What is a species?

The reply to this question often depends on who gives the answer.

- An **ecologist** might reply that all the members of a population belong to the same species. The individuals are very similar to each other and can sexually reproduce offspring which are themselves able to reproduce.
- A **geneticist** might reply that individuals which have a very similar set of genes are members of the same species.
- A **molecular biologist** might reply that individuals which have a very similar genome are members of the same species.

In a sense, all these replies are correct – but the accuracy of their definitions depends on the meaning of 'very similar'. In the case of the ecologist's reply, for example, members of some closely related species are able to breed and reproduce fertile offspring.

Ultimately the difference between species arises from the differences between their genes. But this leads to another question:

- How great must the difference be before individuals are no longer varieties of the same species but different species?
- For example, genetic diversity between the millions of different species of insect is no more than the genetic diversity between the varieties of *Escherichia coli* – a single species of common bacteria found in the human gut!

The problem of definitions means that there is no completely satisfactory answer to the question 'What is a species?'

How science works (H)

Sometimes a living thing has several different everyday names which describe it.

- For example, the plant in this picture is called 'cuckoo pint', 'lords and ladies', 'parson-in-the-pulpit' and 'wake-robin' in different parts of the UK.

On the other hand, different living things are sometimes given the same name.

- For example, the robin in the USA is different from the robin in the UK.

Everyday names cause confusion.

- For example, British and American ornithologists (an ornithologist is someone who studies birds) would not be certain they were communicating information about the same species if they spoke to each other about 'robins'.

Questions

1. Explain the difference between the terms classification and taxonomy.
2. Why do most systems of classification reflect the phylogeny (evolutionary history) of organisms?
3. Describe the pentadactyl arrangement of your left arm and hand.

2.19 Comparing species

O B J E C T I V E S

By the end of the section you should understand that recent developments in the molecular life sciences help to establish the phylogenetic relationships between organisms:

○ *comparing amino acid sequences in specific proteins*

○ *comparing variations in specific proteins using immunological techniques*

○ *comparing DNA base sequences*

○ *DNA–DNA hybridization*

Before you start, it will help to read sections **2.02** (DNA), **2.03** (genes), **2.06** (diversity), **2.07** (haemoglobin), and **2.18** (species).

Homologous characteristics

Recall:

• Organisms are usually classified (put into groups) according to the characteristics they share as a result of inheriting the characteristics from a common ancestor. We say that the characteristics are **homologous**.

• Classifications are usually based on shared homologous characteristics, so they reflect the phylogeny (evolutionary history) and relatedness of the organisms in question.

Data used to identify homologous characteristics have traditionally come from studies of

• anatomy (body structures)

• patterns of the development of embryos

Today, homologous characteristics may also be identified using the methods of the molecular life sciences.

Comparing amino acid sequences in specific proteins

The first protein to have the sequence of its amino acids worked out was insulin, in 1953. The amino acid sequences of other proteins such as haemoglobin are now available.

There are enough sequences of homologous molecules in enough species to make it possible to work out phylogenies and relatedness between groups of organisms.

Different forms of haemoglobin are an example of molecular homology. In other words, the haemoglobins found in different species are a shared characteristic inherited from a common ancestor.

• Species are more closely or more distantly related to each other depending on the number of amino acid differences between species.

• Generally the number of amino acid differences is inversely proportional to the closeness of the relatedness – i.e. the fewer the differences, the more closely related are the species.

Comparing variations in haemoglobin using immunological techniques

Recall:

• B cells in the blood produce antibodies in response to the presence of antigens. This is the immune response.

• Antigens are substances to which antibodies bind. Proteins can act as antigens. Antibodies therefore can bind to proteins.

• Antibody–protein binding depends on the shape of the antigen-binding sites of the antibody molecule matching the shape of the protein (or part of protein). The closer the match between antibody and protein, the more strongly they bind together.

• The shape of a protein depends on the sequence of its amino acids. If one amino acid or more of a particular protein changes then the binding properties of its matching antibody will alter. The more changes in the amino acid sequence of the protein, the less strongly will the antigen bind to the different variants of the protein.

The table shows that the types of amino acid which make up the β-chain of the protein haemoglobin in different species varies. The greater the variation, the more distantly related are the species.

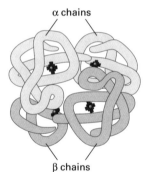

α chains

β chains

Number of amino acid differences in the β-chain of the haemoglobin molecule of different species compared with humans

Human	0
Gorilla	1
Gibbon	2
Rhesus monkey	8
Dog	15
Horse, cow	25
Mouse	27
Gray kangaroo	38
Chicken	45
Frog	67

One way of working out the relatedness of the species to humans is to measure how strongly the antibody which is specific for the β-chain of human haemoglobin binds to the haemoglobins of the other species.

• The stronger the binding, the more closely related is the species to humans.

• The weaker the binding, the more distant is the relationship.

Comparing the base sequences of DNA nucleotides

Working out the base sequences of DNA nucleotides (and the genes they form) and how the base sequences vary is one aspect of **structural genomics**.

By comparing DNA base sequences among species (**comparative genomics**), it is possible to

- identify changes in genes (and whole genomes) as species have evolved
- work out evolutionary relationships among organisms: closely related organisms would be expected to have similar DNA base sequences; less closely related organisms would be expected to have less similar DNA base sequences.

Fact file

Comparing DNA base sequences has led to new classifications of flowering plants. The work is based on two chloroplast genes and one gene encoding ribosomes. Traditionally flowering plants are classified as two large groups depending on the number of cotyledons within the seed:

- monocotyledons (monocots – one cotyledon)
- dicotyledons (dicots – two cotyledons)

DNA analysis suggests a more complex grouping. For example one proposal keeps the names 'monocots/dicots' but subdivides the dicots further.

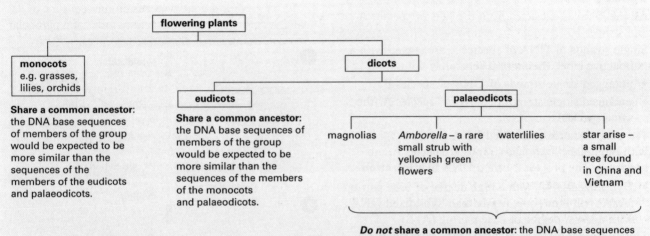

The proposal is only one of several suggested by the new data coming from DNA analysis.

Which sequencing technique is best?

Why work out the base sequences of genes when the amino acid sequence of the proteins which the genes encode is possible?

- It is easier to sequence the bases of genes than the amino acids of proteins.
- There may be more than one base sequence encoding a particular protein (see below).
- In the environment, DNA is more stable than protein. So it is possible to sequence the bases of DNA extracted from fossils of extinct organisms.

Recall that most amino acids are encoded by more than one codon – the genetic code is degenerate. As a result, the base sequence of a gene is much freer to change during evolution than the amino acid sequence of a protein.

- If the codon encoding an amino acid is substituted by another codon which also encodes the same amino acid, then the base sequence of the gene in question

changes but the amino acid sequence of the protein does not.

- As a result, changes in genes during evolution using information from the amino acid sequences of proteins may be missed.
- Changes in the amino acid sequence of proteins are more likely to lead to loss of function than changes in the base sequence of genes.

Fact file

One way of sequencing the bases of DNA is the **chain-termination method**. The process begins by breaking up the chromosomes carrying the DNA into pieces. Single-stranded DNA is separated from the proteins which are part of the structure of the chromosomes. The strands of DNA are cloned, producing millions of copies. The strands are templates against which new strands of DNA are replicated. Sequencing of the DNA bases then begins.

DNA–DNA hybridization

The technique of DNA–DNA hybridization is a way of comparing the total genome of different species.

- It measures the genetic similarities and differences between species.
- The information can then be used to work out the phylogenetic relationships between organisms.

> Recall the base-pairing rules:
>
> - Adenine (A) always bonds with thymine (T).
>   A–T   T–A
> - Guanine (G) always bonds with cytosine (C).
>   G–C   C–G

Comparing species A with species B

The diagram summarizes the technique of DNA–DNA hydridization.

① All the DNA is extracted from the cells of species A and species B.

② Single strands of DNA of species A are tagged with a radioactive label, then mixed separately with
- untagged single strands of DNA of species B
- untagged single strands of DNA of species A (the same species)

③ The single strands of labelled DNA (species A) bind with the unlabelled single strands of species A and species B. The process is called **DNA hybridization**.

- Hybridized DNA with a high degree of base pairing (A/A) will bind more firmly than hybridized DNA with a lesser degree of base pairing (A/B)

④ The mixtures (A/A) and (A/B) are each individually heated in small steps (2°–3°C). Heating separates the double-stranded hybrids (A/A), (A/B). The process is called **DNA melting**.

- Double-stranded hybrids formed from the same species (A/A) each bind more firmly than double-stranded hybrids formed from different species (A/B). So more energy (heat) is needed to separate strands A/A than strands A/B.
- At each higher temperature, a small sample of each mixture is passed through a column of material to which double-stranded DNA binds but single-stranded DNA (produced by melting) can pass through when the column is 'washed'.
- The proportion of single-stranded DNA in each mixture washed from the column at each temperature is a measure of how firmly DNA strands have hybridized. More single-stranded DNA will wash from the A/B (x+, y+, z+%) column than the A/A (x, y, z%) column at lower temperatures.
- The amount of single-stranded DNA washed from each column at each temperature is measured from the radioactivity of each sample.

⑤ The temperature at which 50% of the A/B hybrid and A/A hybrid combinations have melted to produce single strands of DNA is calculated. The difference in temperature is a measure of the relatedness of the DNA between species A and B. The smaller the difference, the more closely are the two species related.

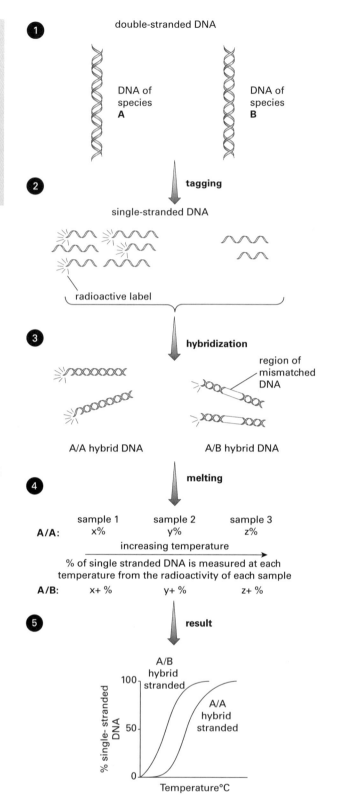

Questions

1. Explain why comparing DNA base sequences is the preferred method of establishing the phylogenetic relationships between organisms.
2. Summarize the technique of DNA–DNA hybridization.

2.20 Courtship behaviour

OBJECTIVES

By the end of the section you should

○ *understand that courtship behaviour is a prelude to sexual reproduction*

○ *know that courtship behaviour involves finding and selecting a mate of the same species*

Before you start, it will help to read section **2.18** (species).

Courting behaviour refers to the interactions between males and females of the same species which lead to copulation, the conception of offspring, and in many species their subsequent care. Its components include:

*   attraction of mates
*   behaviour which enables individuals to recognize a potential partner as the opposite sex and correct species
*   synchronization of sexual behaviour between partners
*   care of the offspring by one or both parents.

In sticklebacks (a type of fish), for example, one component leads to the next – the behaviour of an individual causes a response in the partner. The flow diagram shows the sequence of events.

Notice:

*   Nuptial colours in the male are sign stimuli which either cause
    (a) aggressive behaviour between males, or
    (b) attraction between males and females.
*   A sign stimulus in one individual releases behaviour in another individual. The behaviour is also a sign stimulus to which the first individual responds... and so on.

If the sign stimuli and the responses to them are inappropriate, then the sequence of behaviour breaks down. Courtship stops and sexual activity followed by conception does not take place.

Courtship behaviour therefore

*   enables individuals of the species to recognize one another
*   promotes **pre-zygotic isolation** (i.e. the chances of sexual activity between individuals of different species leading to conception is reduced)
    *   as a result the chances of hybridization are reduced
    *   as a result the characteristics which are unique to and identify a species are maintained

However, recall that there are many exceptions and that the meaning of the term 'species' is problematical.

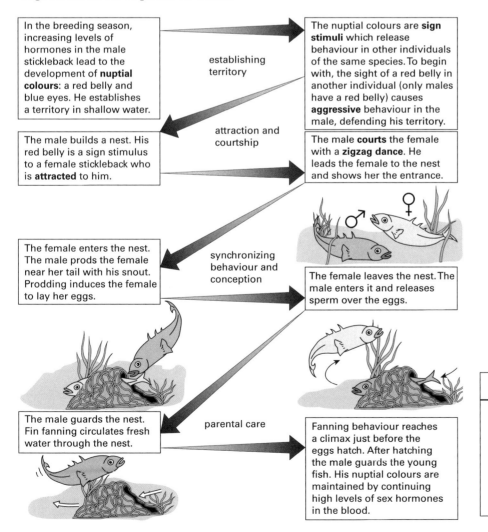

In the breeding season, increasing levels of hormones in the male stickleback lead to the development of **nuptial colours**: a red belly and blue eyes. He establishes a territory in shallow water.

establishing territory

The nuptial colours are **sign stimuli** which release behaviour in other individuals of the same species. To begin with, the sight of a red belly in another individual (only males have a red belly) causes **aggressive** behaviour in the male, defending his territory.

attraction and courtship

The male builds a nest. His red belly is a sign stimulus to a female stickleback who is **attracted** to him.

The male **courts** the female with a **zigzag dance**. He leads the female to the nest and shows her the entrance.

The female enters the nest. The male prods the female near her tail with his snout. Prodding induces the female to lay her eggs.

synchronizing behaviour and conception

The female leaves the nest. The male enters it and releases sperm over the eggs.

The male guards the nest. Fin fanning circulates fresh water through the nest.

parental care

Fanning behaviour reaches a climax just before the eggs hatch. After hatching the male guards the young fish. His nuptial colours are maintained by continuing high levels of sex hormones in the blood.

Questions

1 Identify the components of courtship behaviour.

2 What are sign stimuli?

3 How does courtship behaviour promote pre-zygotic isolation?

2.21 Antibiotics and genetic variation in bacteria

OBJECTIVES

By the end of the section you should

○ *know that antibiotics are used to treat bacterial diseases*

○ *understand how bacteria may develop resistance to antibiotics*

○ *know that the development of resistance makes it difficult to treat tuberculosis and MRSA*

○ *understand some of the ethical issues associated with the use of antibiotics*

Before you start, it will help to read sections **1.01** (pathogens), **1.13** (cholera), and **2.03** (genes).

Types of antibiotic

Before the discovery of antibiotic drugs in the 1920s, bacterial diseases killed many people. Thanks to antibiotics most bacterial diseases up to now can be cured.

There are two sorts of antibiotic:

- **bactericides** like penicillin which kill bacteria
- **bacteristats** like tetracycline which prevent bacteria from multiplying

Different antibiotics affect bacteria in different ways.

- Bactericides mostly damage the structure of the bacterial cell. For example some bactericides prevent the formation of the bacterial cell wall. Osmosis floods the cells with water. The increase in hydrostatic pressure bursts the cells, resulting in **osmotic lysis**.
- Bacteristats mostly disrupt the chemical reactions taking place in the bacterial cell.

The diagram shows how different antibiotics affect bacteria.

Resistance

Genes are particular sections of DNA which control the synthesis of proteins, and so control the characteristics of organisms.

- Mutations in DNA alter genes, and so alter the proteins (and characteristics) for which the DNA codes.
- The genetic material in bacteria is DNA. Mutations in bacterial DNA may lead to new characteristics, including the development of resistance to antibiotics.

Bacterial resistance to antibiotics appeared soon after their first use to treat diseases caused by bacteria. Today some diseases, including tuberculosis, are difficult to treat with antibiotics. Bacteria resistant to all currently used antibiotics can only be treated with experimental, and possibly very poisonous, alternatives.

Unless the problems of antibiotic resistance are detected early on, then bacterial diseases which previously could be treated may become untreatable. For example, *Staphylococcus aureus* causes boils and food poisoning. Hospital strains of the bacterium are resistant to virtually all known antibiotics.

How does resistance develop?

Some types of bacteria are inherently resistant to antibiotics. For example, the capsule which surrounds some types of bacterial cell is a barrier to antibiotics. Other types of bacteria, previously sensitive to antibiotics, may acquire resistance through changes in the bacterial genetic material. The process is driven by two processes:

Mutation

- Mutated genes which confer resistance are inherited by offspring from parent cells in which the mutation occurred.
- The mutation may spread very rapidly because a new generation of bacterial cells inheriting the mutation may be reproduced every 20 minutes or so.
- **Vertical gene transmission** refers to the inheritance of resistance genes from parental cells to offspring.

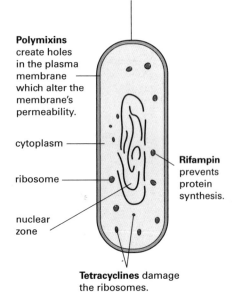

Penicillin and **cephalosporins** prevent the bacterium from making components of the cell wall, which is therefore weakened. The bacterium is then more easily destroyed by immune reactions.

Polymixins create holes in the plasma membrane which alter the membrane's permeability.

cytoplasm

ribosome

nuclear zone

Rifampin prevents protein synthesis.

Tetracyclines damage the ribosomes.

How different antibiotics affect bacteria

Fact file

Darwinian evolution through natural selection is one route by which bacterial resistance to antibiotics develops. In hospitals the selection pressure of antibiotics is so intense that strains of bacteria quickly evolve resistance to a range of antibiotics.

Exchange of resistance genes

Resistance genes are exchanged between different strains of a species of bacterium or between different species of bacteria. The genes exchanged confer resistance on the bacteria acquiring them.

- **Transduction** occurs when viruses which only infect bacteria transfer genes between two closely related bacteria.
- **Transformation** occurs when bacteria take up genes from their immediate environment.
- **Conjugation** occurs when two bacteria make direct cell-to-cell contact. Plasmids containing resistance genes may pass from one cell to the other.

Horizontal gene transmission refers to the transfer of genes between unrelated bacterial cells. The diagram summarizes the processes.

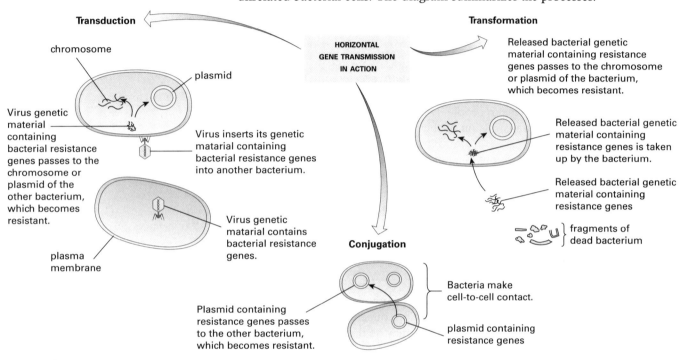

Horizontal gene transmission

How do bacteria resist antibiotics?

Different mechanisms confer bacteria with antibiotic resistance.

- Inactivation by bacterial enzymes which make antibiotics ineffective is the most common.
- Alternatively the antibiotic's target in the bacterial cell alters so that the cell is no longer affected by the antibiotic.

The diagram summarizes other mechanisms of antibiotic resistance.

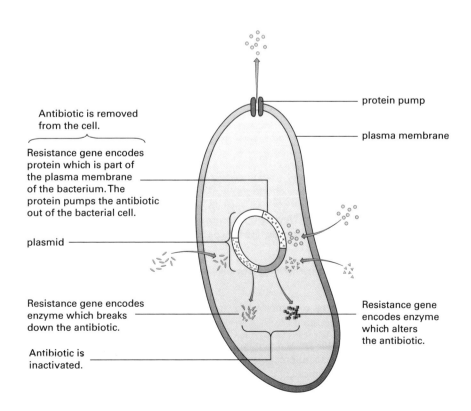

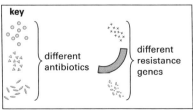

Bacterial resistance mechanisms

Why is treating TB and MRSA with antibiotics difficult?

Tuberculosis

There was no cure for tuberculosis (TB) before the discovery of antibiotics which killed the bacterium that caused the disease. The introduction of anti-TB drugs in the 1950s meant that by the 1980s there was a 98% chance of a cure.

However, cure requires

- expensive drugs taken in combination
- long-term treatment (up to 6 months)

These cures are often beyond the reach of countries where TB is common and health care poor. The difficulties have allowed the development of strains of the tubercular bacterium which are resistant to a number of drugs.

The treatment of multi-drug resistant tuberculosis is complicated and expensive. Problems include:

- the diagnosis of drug resistant patients
- HIV infection which weakens the immune system, accelerating the development of TB infection into TB disease
- homelessness which may mean people living in crowded, unhygienic conditions, making the transmission of the tubercular bacterium between people more likely
- making sure that TB patients follow medical advice and continue to take the 3–4 drugs needed in the long term to give the best possible chance of a cure

Once the best combination of drugs has been identified, one of the most effective (and cheapest) approaches is **directly observed therapy**. The patient takes their medication under the eye of a trained supervisor.

MRSA

Staphylococcus aureum (SA) is found on the surface of skin or in the nose. About 1 in 3 people carry the bacterium – usually without problems. But if it enters the body, boils and abscesses may develop. Infection of the blood is even more serious; septicaemia and toxic shock may be the fatal result.

Methicillin (a type of penicillin) is the drug of choice used to treat *SA* infections. But strains of the bacterium are now resistant to the drug – these are called methicillin-resistant SA (**MRSA**).

MRSA-infected people may need

- a much higher dose of methicillin
- treatment in hospital over a longer period
- to take antibiotics to which the MRSA bacteria are not resistant

Prevention is better than cure and high standards of hospital hygiene are the first line of defence.

Fact file

Antibiotics are big business. Developing new ones to combat resistance is expensive. Many countries struggle to finance the expertise, new drugs, and education needed.

- Expertise enables the methodology, evidence, and data relating to antibiotic resistance to be evaluated.
- New (expensive) drugs can improve the treatment of diseases which have become antibiotic resistant.
- Education enables the general population to understand the science behind antibiotic resistance to different diseases, and make informed decisions about the use of new antibiotics.

These are some of the ethical issues associated with the use of antibiotics.

Questions

1 Briefly explain two ways in which antibiotics function to treat bacterial disease.

2 How might bacteria develop resistance to antibiotics?

3 Explain the difference between vertical gene transmission and horizontal gene transmission.

2.22 Species diversity

How science works (G)

Uncertainties of definition

The index of diversity is not only a measure of species diversity. It is also a measure of genetic diversity. However, uncertainties of the relationship between genetic diversity and the definition of species make the use of the index of diversity as a measure of biodiversity a problem.

How science works (J)

Sustaining the rain forests

Large-scale clearance of rain forest makes way for cattle ranches. Growing grass for the cattle to eat soon exhausts the soil of nutrients. Spreading fertilizer over such large areas of cleared forest is too expensive. The ranches are abandoned and the environment quickly turns to semi-desert.

It is possible to manage tropical rain forests for human benefit while keeping the environment intact. Perhaps the rubber-tappers of the Amazon rain forest point the way. They collect rubber, nuts, and fruits and hunt in an organized way, so that these products are not used up faster than they can be replaced naturally.

Their methods use the rain forest as a resource which renews itself in a sustainable way. In the long term, more money is made per hectare of forest than with large-scale ranching, which is unsustainable because the soil is quickly exhausted of the nutrients needed for plant growth.

Biodiversity and the index of diversity

So far, biologists have described and named more than 5 million species of organisms. However the figure is only a fraction of the estimated millions of species yet to be discovered. So the classifications of taxonomists are inventories of the diversity of species. The term **biodiversity** refers to species diversity.

One definition of biodiversity includes the relationship between all of the species in a community of organisms and the numbers of each species. An **index of diversity** describes the relationship.

* Different species may be active within the community all of the time while others may be active only at particular times.
* The definition also includes the interactions between species.

A measure of biodiversity can be calculated from the formula

$$d = \frac{N(N-1)}{\Sigma n(n-1)}$$

Where:

d = index of diversity

Σ = sum of

N = total number of organisms of all species

n = total number of organisms of each species

The index of diversity is

* *low* in environments hostile to survival (e.g. hot deserts) where conditions may change quickly and the community is mostly affected by climate, type of soil, and other so-called abiotic factors
* *high* in environments favourable to survival (e.g. tropical rain forests) where conditions change only slowly and the community is mostly affected by interactions between species and other so-called biotic factors.

Human impact on species diversity

The extinction of species through human activities reduces species diversity and so reduces genetic diversity. It also reduces the possibility of exploiting genetic material for the improvement of crops and the development of new medicines.

Historically, the destruction of habitats has driven many species to extinction. Continuing growth of the human population increases pressure for yet more land to produce the food needed to feed people. Habitats continue to be destroyed along with the species occupying them.

* **Deforestation** – Cutting down large areas of forest prevents regeneration of the plants removed. Destruction of the plants destroys the habitats of animals and other organisms.
  * As a result species are driven to extinction.
  * As a result species diversity is reduced.
* **Agriculture** – Apart from the demand for land, **selective breeding** reduces the number of varieties of crops and animals raised for food.

If the conditions in which crops and animals are raised alter in the future, then the selective breeding of new varieties able to survive the changed conditions many not be possible. Why? Because there is a smaller pool of genes to draw from.

Questions

1 What does the index of diversity measure?

2 How may uncertainties of the definition of species affect the reliability of the index of diversity?

3 Summarize the human impact on species diversity.

Unit 1 questions

1 Match each cell structure with the correct description.

Cell structure	Description

Cell structure

A ribosome
B cell wall
C vacuole
D mitochondrion
E nucleus
F starch grain
G plasma membrane
H endoplasmic reticulum
I glycogen
J chloroplast

Description

a contains genetic material
b contains cell sap
c where aerobic respiration takes place
d a food reserve in animal cells
e where photosynthesis takes place
f where protein synthesis takes place
g made of cellulose
h controls movement of substances into and out of cells
i network of channels running through the cytoplasm
j a food reserve in plant cells

2 The diagram shows a type of bacterium which causes food poisoning.

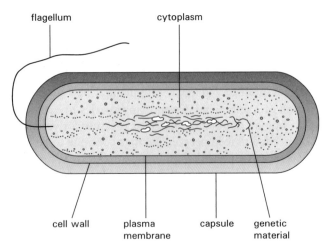

a Give **one** similarity and identify **three** differences between the structure of the bacterial cell and the structure of a palisade cell in a leaf.

b How is the genetic material in bacterial cells organized?

3 In times of war, opponents try to disrupt the other side's food supplies. For example, the Romans scattered salt in the wheat fields of their opponents, destroying the plants. Repeating the experiment today and sampling the tissues of plants treated and untreated with salt, the cells of sampled tissues seen under the optical microscope would appear like this:

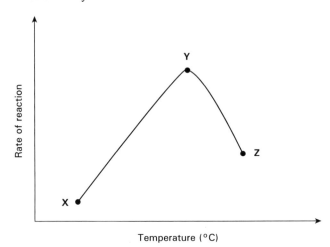

a Describe the appearance of the cytoplasm of each cell.

b Explain why the appearance of the cytoplasm in each cell is different.

4 The graph shows how temperature affects the rate of an enzyme-controlled reaction.

a Explain the change in the rate of reaction between:
  i X and Y
  ii Y and Z

b How might high temperature affect the active site of the enzyme?

5 Match these substances with their functions.

Substance

A collagen
B cellulose
C glycerol
D phospholipid
E starch
F fructose

Function

a part of cell membranes
b same molecular formula as glucose
c main component of ligaments and tendons
d forms a triglyceride with 3 molecules of fatty acid
e a component of the wall of plant cells
f stored in plant cells

6 The diagram represents two alveoli and a blood capillary in lung tissue.

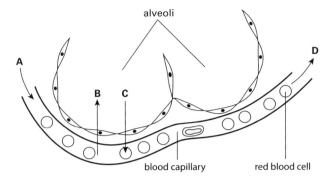

alveoli

A

B C

blood capillary red blood cell

D

a Which arrow represents
  i deoxygenated blood?
  ii carbon dioxide?
b **i** Explain the process by which oxygen passes from the air in the alveoli to the red blood cells in the capillary.
  ii Through how many layers of cells does the oxygen pass?

7 The diagram shows a section through the human heart viewed from the front.

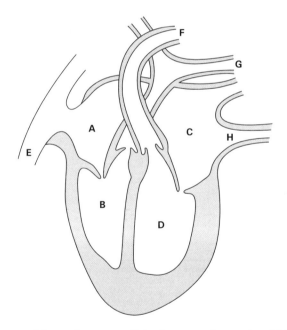

F

G

A C

H

E

B

D

a Name the parts of the heart and associated blood vessels labelled A–H.
b Which **two** parts of the heart show that the chambers A and C are relaxed?
c Why is the wall of chamber D thicker than the wall of chamber B?

8 The diagram shows lengthways sections of a healthy blood vessel and a diseased blood vessel.

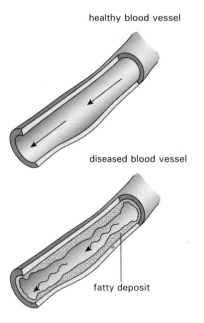

healthy blood vessel

diseased blood vessel

fatty deposit

a What is the fatty deposit called?
b The artery narrows where the fatty deposit is forming. Briefly explain how the blood vessel could become completely blocked.
c What is a heart attack?

9 Monoclonal antibodies attached to a radioactive label are used to locate cancerous cells in the body.
  a How can the antibodies be detected when they have located the cancerous cells?
  b Once the cancerous cells are located they can be destroyed by drugs attached to the monoclonal antibodies without the drugs damaging healthy cells. Explain how this happens.

Unit 2 questions

10 The diagram represents the movement of tissue fluid, plasma, and lymph between capillary blood vessels, cells of tissues, and lymph vessels.

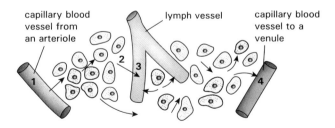

capillary blood vessel from an arteriole   lymph vessel   capillary blood vessel to a venule

1   2   3   4

a Name the fluid in each of the locations numbered 1–4.
b Explain why fluid leaves the capillary blood vessels at 1, but enters the capillary blood vessel at 4.

11 The diagram represents a plan for organizing living things into groups. Use the correct terms to fill in the blank spaces. Two spaces have been filled in for you.

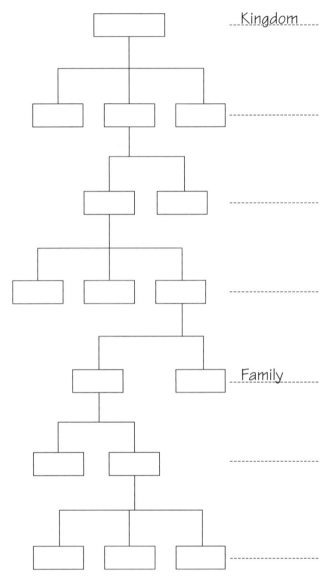

Kingdom

Family

12 The diagram represents part of a DNA molecule.

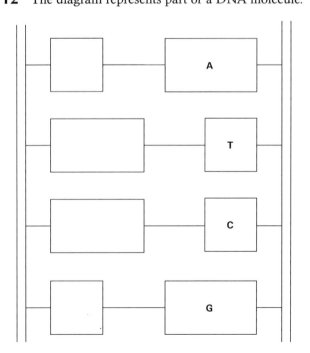

The letters represent the bases adenine (A), thymine (T), cytosine (C), and guanine (G).

a Complete the empty boxes with the letter of the correct base.

b Indicate with an arrow which chemical bonds break when replication of the molecule takes place.

c Name the enzyme which catalyses the breaking of the bonds.

d At what stage in the cell cycle does DNA replicate?

13 In a population of 300 goldfish, variations in two characteristics were measured and the results represented as charts. Chart A shows the variation in length of fish; chart B shows variation in their colour.

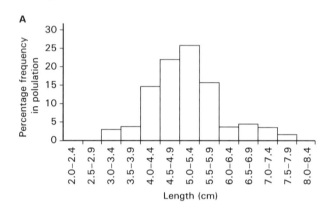

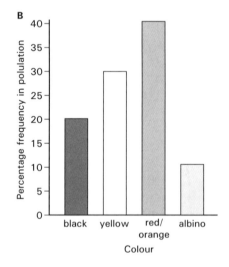

a Which chart shows

i continuous variation?

ii discontinuous variation?

Briefly give reasons for your answers.

b Using chart B calculate the percentage of yellow goldfish in the population.

c Albino goldfish are relatively rare compared with the colours of the other fish. Give a genetic explanation for the occurrence of albino goldfish.

14 Rose flowers form fruits following fertilization. All the fruits from five rose bushes of the same species were collected and their lengths measured. The results are shown in the table.

Rose bush	Length of fruit (mm)
1	14, 18, 13, 16, 16, 13, 17, 19, 11, 19
2	12, 15, 19, 18, 15, 16, 18, 14, 19, 19
3	16, 15, 16, 14, 18, 14, 15, 18, 20, 15
4	15, 17, 14, 12, 16, 20, 19, 17, 15, 16
5	15, 13, 15, 19, 18, 20, 14, 19, 19, 14

a Draw a graph or chart to represent the data. Explain your choice.

b Variation in the length of the rose fruits is due to environmental factors. Describe the possible causes for the variation in fruit length.

c Some of the seeds inside the rose fruits germinate and grow into rose bushes, which also produce fruits. Explain why the variation in fruit length of the parent rosebush due to environmental factors will not affect the fruit length of their offspring.

15 The bar chart shows the rate of blood flow to different organs of the body.

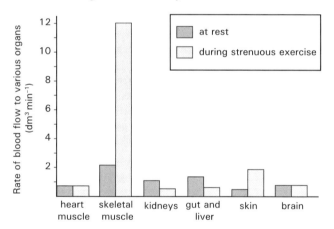

a What is the volume of blood per minute being pumped by the left ventricle to the different organs when the body is:

i at rest?

ii strenuously exercising?

b Explain the link between the decrease in blood supply to the kidneys, gut, and liver and the increase in blood supply to the skeletal muscle during strenuous exercise.

16 The letters represent the sequence of bases of a short length of a strand of DNA.

A A T C C T G A C T A G G A T

a How many codons are represented in the strand of DNA? (Start at the left of the strand and assume that codons do not overlap.)

b How many amino acid units are encoded by the strand of DNA?

c Explain why the substitution of one of the bases in the strand with another different base need not unnecessarily alter the sequence of amino acids.

d If the number of amino acid units form a whole molecule, which term would best describe the molecule – **protein**, **peptide** or **polypeptide**?

17 Phenylthiocarbamide is a substance which tastes bitter to some people but not others. The table shows the frequency of 'non-tasters' in different groups of people.

Group	'Non tasters' (%)
Hindus	33.7
Danish	32.7
British	31.5
Spanish	25.6
Portuguese	24.0
Japanese	7.1
Lapps	6.4
West Africans	2.7
Chinese	2.0
S. American (indigenous people)	1.2

a Is people's response to phenylthiocarbamide an example of continuous or discontinuous variation?

b Give a genetic explanation for the differences in responses to phenylthiocarbamide between different groups of people.

Answers to further practice questions

1 ribosome – where protein synthesis takes place

cell wall – made of cellulose

vacuole – contains cell sap

mitochondrion – where aerobic respiration takes place

nucleus – contains genetic material

starch grain – a food reserve in plant cells

plasma membrane – controls movement of substances into and out of cells

endoplasmic reticulum – network of channels running through the cytoplasm

glycogen – a food reserve in animal cells

chloroplast – where photosynthesis takes place

2 a Similarity – any one of: cell wall, cytoplasm, plasma membrane

Differences – flagellum, capsule, (accept) cell wall, (do not accept made of cellulose)

b As strands and loops called plasmids, not surrounded by a nuclear membrane

3 a Cell A – The plasma membrane surrounding the cytoplasm is pressed against the cell wall.

Cell B – The plasma membrane surrounding the cytoplasm has drawn away from the cell wall.

b The water potential of the cytoplasm of cell A is more negative than the environment outside the cell. Water therefore passes by osmosis from the outside into the cell, down a water potential gradient. The increase in hydrostatic pressure within the cell presses the cytoplasm against the cell wall.

The water potential of the cytoplasm of cell B is less negative than the environment outside the cell. Water therefore passes by osmosis from inside the cell to the outside. The decrease in hydrostatic pressure within the cell allows the cytoplasm to draw away from the cell wall.

4 a i Between X and Y the rate of reaction increases as the temperature increases.

ii Between Y and Z the increasing denaturation of enzyme results in a decrease in the rate of reaction.

b By altering the structure (and therefore shape) of the active site of the enzyme so that substrate molecules can no longer bind to the active site.

5 collagen – main component of ligaments and tendons

cellulose – a component of the wall of plant cells

glycerol – forms a triglyceride with 3 molecules of fatty acid

phospholipid – part of cell membranes

starch – stored in plant cells

fructose – same molecular formula as glucose

6 a i A **ii** B

b i Diffusion – the concentration of oxygen in the air in the alveoli is greater than the concentration of oxygen in the blood. Oxygen therefore passes down the oxygen concentration gradient from the alveoli to the blood.

ii 2

7 a A = right atrium, B = right ventricle, C = left atrium, D = left ventricle, E = vena cava,

F = aorta, G = pulmonary artery, H = pulmonary vein

b Tricuspid and bicuspid valves closed; semi-lunar valves open.

8 a Atheroma

b The build-up of atheroma makes the blood vessel narrower and cuts down the flow of blood. The roughened lining and slower blood flow increase the risk of blood clotting.

c A heart attack happens when the flow of blood to the heart is interrupted.

9 a Emissions from the radioactive label

b The drugs only affect the cells to which the monoclonal antibodies carrying the drugs become attached. The antibodies only attach to the cancerous cells and not to healthy cells. Therefore the cancerous cells are destroyed by the drugs but the healthy cells are unaffected.

10 a 1 = plasma, 2 = tissue fluid, 3 = lymph, 4 = plasma

b At 1, the hydrostatic pressure (which forces small molecules through the walls of the capillary vessels into the tissues) at the arteriole end is greater than the colloid osmotic pressure (which tends to draw molecules back into the blood capillaries). Therefore there is a net outflow of substances in solution from the capillaries into the tissues.

At 4, the hydrostatic pressure at the venule end is less than the colloid osmotic pressure. Therefore there is a net movement of substances in solution into the capillaries.

11 [Kingdom], phylum, class, order, [family], genus, species

12 a TAGC

b Arrows pointing to the four bonds which join T–A, A–T, G–C and C–G

c DNA helicase

d The S stage of interphase

13 a i A

ii B

(Chart A shows all intermediate lengths between the extremes of length. There are no intermediate colours for the categories of colour in chart B.)

b 30%

c A mutation of the gene(s) controlling colour of fish

14 a The data is best represented as a bar chart because it is discontinuous.

b Temperature, supply of nutrients in the soil, availability of water

c Seeds are the result of sexual reproduction and so variation in the offspring will be the result of genetic causes; environmental causes of variation in fruit length of parent plants will not affect the gametes of the parent plants and therefore cannot be inherited.

15 a

	Volume of blood (dm³min⁻¹)	
	At home	During strenuous exercise
Heart muscle	0.5	0.8
Skeletal muscle	2.2	2.0
Kidneys	1.4	0.7
Gut and liver	1.6	0.8
Skin	0.7	2.1
Brain	0.8	0.8

b The rate of blood flow to these organs decreases as blood is diverted to the skeletal muscle (and heart muscle).

16 a 5

b 5

c Because the genetic code is degenerate

d Peptide

17 a Discontinuous variation

b The frequency of distribution of the gene(s) which determines an individual's ability to taste phenylthiocarbamide varies between different groups of people.

INDEX

absorption, 33
activation energy, 18
active site, 18
active transport, 32
adaptation, 68–9, 74–5
adenine, 56
aerobic respiration, 77
agglutination, 45
allosteric inhibition, 19
alpha (α) helix, 105
alveoli, 36, 76
amino acids, 15, 90
Amoeba proteus, gas exchange, 77
amylase, 22
amylose, 66
amylopectin, 66
angina, 43
antibiotics, 94–6
antibodies, 45, 46
antigens, 45
antigenic drift/shift, 48
antiports, 32, 35
apoplastic route, 85
arteries, 82
arterioles, 83
asbestosis, 38
asthma, 39
atheroma, 43
atherosclerosis, 43
ATP, 32
atrial diastole/systole, 41

B cells, 45–7
bacteria, 10
bacteria, genetic variation, 94–6
bactericides, 94
bacteristats, 94
Benedict's test, 21
beta (β) pleated sheet, 16
binomial system, 88
biodiversity, 97
biuret test, 17
bivalent, 61
blood pressure, 11, 12
blood system, 82–4
blood vessels, 83
Bohr effect, 65
bony fish, gas exchange, 80
breathing, 36–7
bronchioles, 36
brush border, 33
Bundle of His, 41

cancer, 11, 13, 71–3
capillaries, 82, 83–4
capillary beds, 83–4
carbohydrases, 22–3
carbohydrate digestion, 22–3
carbohydrates, 20–1
carcinogens, 13, 72–3
cardiac arrest, 44
cardiac cycle, 41
cardiac muscle, 40
carrier proteins, 33
Casparian strip, 86
catalysts, 18
cell cycle, 71–3
cell differentiation, 74–5
cell division, 71–2
cell structure, 26, 68–9
cell walls, 69
cells, 24–5, 26, 34, 45–8, 68–9
cellular respiration, 67, 77
cellulose, 20, 66–7
centrifugation, 24–5
centromere, 59
cerebral haemorrhage, 12
chain-termination method, 91

chemotherapy, 73
chiasma, 54
chloroplasts, 69
cholera, 34–5
cholesterol, 12, 43
chromatids, 54, 59
chromatin, 59, 71
chromosomes, 54–5, 59
circulatory system, 82
classification, 88–9
cohesion–tension theory, 87
collagen, 17
colloid osmotic pressure, 84
companion cells, 69
compensation point, 78
competitive inhibitors, 19
complementary base pairing, 57
concentration gradient, 30
condensation, 15, 20
conjugation, 95
continuous variation, 53
coronary arteries, 43
cortex, 69, 85
co-transport, 33
courtship behaviour, 93
cytokinesis, 60, 72
cytoplasm, 26
cytosine, 56
cytoskeleton, 28

daughter cells, 60, 71
deaths, causes of, 11
deforestation, 97
deoxyribonucleic acid (DNA), 52, 56–7, 59, 94
diarrhoea, 34
diastolic blood pressure, 12
diet, 11–12, 22
differentiation, 74, 85
diffusion, 30–2, 77
digestion, 14, 22–3
digestive system, 14
dipeptides, 15
diphtheria, 10
diploid, 60–1
disaccharides, 20
discontinuous variation, 53
diseases, 10, 11–13, 38–9, 43–4
dissociation curves, 64–5
diversity, 62–3, 97
division furrow, 72
DNA, 52, 56–7, 59, 91, 94
DNA helicase, 70
DNA melting, 92
DNA nucleotides, 91
DNA polymerase, 70
DNA replication, 70
DNA–DNA hybridization, 92
double helix, 56–7
Down's syndrome, 55

electrocardiogram (ECG), 42
electron microscopes, 24
embryonic stem cells, 74
emphysema, 39
emulsion test, 28
endodermis, 85
endoplasmic reticulum, 26
endotoxins, 10
enzymes, 10, 18–19
enzyme–substrate complexes, 18
epidemics, 48
epithelia, 22–23, 74–5
exhalation, 37
exons, 58
exotoxins, 10

facilitated diffusion, 30–1
fats, 27

fatty acids, 27
fertilization, 61
fibrosis, 38
fibrous proteins, 17
Fick's law, 30
fish, gas exchange, 80
fluid mosaic membranes, 29
food stores, 67
founder effect, 62–3
fractionation, 24–5
fructose, 20

gas exchange, 77–81
gated pores, 30
gene flow, 62
gene pool, 62
gene therapy, 73
gene transmission, 94–5
genes, 13, 56, 58, 74, 95
genetic bottleneck, 63
genetic code, 58
genetic diversity, 62–3
genetic maps, 58
genetic variation, 54–5, 61, 94–6
genomics, 91
gills, 80
globular proteins, 17, 64
glucose, 20, 33
glycogen, 20, 66–7
glycolipids, 28–9
glycoproteins, 28–9
glycosidic bonds, 20
Golgi apparatus, 26
guanine, 56
guard cells, 78–9
gut, 14

haemoglobin, 11, 64–5, 90
haploid, 60–1
HDL (high density lipoproteins), 12
heart, structure and function, 40–2
heart attacks, 44
heart disease, 11–12, 13, 43–4
heart rate, 42
heartbeat, 40, 42
α-helices, 16
heparin, 43
herd effect, 50
high density lipoproteins (HDL), 12
histones, 59
homologous characteristics, 90
horizontal gene transmission, 95
human immunodeficiency virus (HIV), 10
hydrolysis, 15, 20, 22
hypertension, 12

immune complexes, 45–6
immune response, 45
immune system, 45
immunological memory, 48
immunology, principles, 45–8
independent assortment, 61
index of diversity, 97
induced fit hypothesis, 18
influenza virus, 48
inhalation, 37
inhibition, 19
insects, gas exchange, 81
interferon, 47
interphase, 71
intestines, 14, 22
introns, 58
iodine test, 21
ionization, 73
isomers 20

lactase, 23
lactose, 20, 21